HEBES
AND PARAHEBES

OTHER GARDENING BOOKS PUBLISHED BY CHRISTOPHER HELM

An Anthology of Garden Writing
Edited by Ursula Buchan

Conifers
Keith D. Rushforth

The Conservatory Handbook
Ann Bonar

The Cottage Garden Year
Roy Genders

Creating a Chinese Garden
David H. Engel

The Flower Show
E.D. Wearn

Growing Begonias
E. Catterall

Growing Bulbs
Martyn Rix

Growing Chrysanthemums
Harry Randall and Alan Wren

Growing Cyclamen
Gay Nightingale

Growing Dahlias
Philip Damp

Growing Fuchsias
K. Jennings and V. Miller

Growing Hardy Perennials
Kenneth A. Beckett

Growing Irises
G.E. Cassidy and S. Linnegar

Growing Lilies
Derek Fox

A Handbook of Annuals and Bedding Plants
Graham Rice

The Handbook of Soft Fruit Growing
Ken Muir and David Turner

Hardy Geraniums
Peter F. Yeo

The History of Gardens
Christopher Thacker

Miniature and Dwarf Geraniums
Harold Bagust

Plants for Problem Places
Graham Rice

The Rock Gardener's Handbook
Alan Titchmarsh

Waterlilies
Philip Swindells

The Winter Flower Garden
Sonia Kinahan

HEBES
AND PARAHEBES

Douglas Chalk

CHRISTOPHER HELM
London

TIMBER PRESS
Portland, Oregon

THE CAXTON PRESS
Christchurch, New Zealand

© 1988 Douglas Chalk
Colour plates by Valerie Price
Line illustrations by Eleanor Catherine
Maps by David Henderson and Caroline Minnis
Christopher Helm (Publishers) Ltd, Imperial House,
21-25 North Street, Bromley, Kent BR1 1SD

British Library Cataloguing in Publication Data

Chalk, Douglas
    Hebes and Parahebes.
    1. Hebes
    I.   Title
    635.9'3381   SB413.H4/

    ISBN 0.7470-0410-2

First published in North America in 1988 by
Timber Press
9999 SW Wilshire
Portland, Oregon, 97225
USA

ISBN 0-88192-124-6

Published in New Zealand by
THE CAXTON PRESS
113 Victoria Street, Christchurch

ISBN 0-908563-21-3

Title page: HEBE, *Greek Goddess of Youth and Cup Bearer to the Senior Gods in Olympus. Today, her name
is carried by a genus of plants, in their own way just as beautiful and as useful to the gardener.*
    *It was in October 1926, in New Zealand, that Doctors L. Cockayne and H.H. Allan recognised the
distinctness of these evergreen shrubby Veronicas and classified them under the genus* Hebe. *As other
countries have been slow to recognise this change of name, so too have been the gardeners, both in Britain, the
USA and in New Zealand, in exploring the uses in their gardens of this Goddess amongst plants.*

Printed and bound in Great Britain
by Biddles Ltd, Guildford, Surrey

CONTENTS

Colour plates

═Black and white illustrations═

Acknowledgements

1970 saw the start of my Hebe journey, following an informal meeting at the University of Bath, and has led me to many Gardens and Nurseries in the British Isles, as well as to New Zealand to see Hebes in the wild and in their Parks and Gardens. On the way many people have been helpful to me, including Mr Christopher Brickell of the Royal Horticultural Society, Mr Brian Cook, Mr R. Fulcher when at Inverewe Gardens, Mr Phillip Garnock-Jones of DSIR, Christchurch, NZ, Mr Graham Hutchins of County Park Nursery, Mr Christopher Lloyd of Great Dixter, Mr R. Mole of Otari Native Plant Museum, Wellington, NZ, Dr Mark Smith (deceased), University of Bristol Botanic Garden, Mr Peter Smith and many more. To them all, I am more than grateful.

My sincere thanks to Mr John Collier and Mr Wilfred Simcox for providing and exchanging plants and to Mr Kenneth Beckett for help with identification in the early stages.

I am more than indebted to Mr Lawrie J. Metcalf, Director of Parks and Recreation Department, Invercargill City Corporation, NZ, for reading the manuscript and giving helpful criticisms and for the invaluable Hebe botanical information since 1978. To those in search of botanical information, a Flora is a necessity and it is fortunate that as far as the New Zealand species are concerned, we are indebted to Dr H.H. Allan and Dr Lucy Moore for *Flora of New Zealand*, Volume 1. I have found this a help, not only over the years, but in identifying and describing some of the lesser known Hebes.

My thanks are also due to Mr Graham Rice, the Series Editor, for his suggestions on presentation; Mr Peter Ellis of Pelco Fertilizers, Bath, for the use of the photograph of the delightful Carrara Marble Statue of the Goddess Hebe that he produces (the reproduction statue shown on the title page can be obtained from Peter Ellis at 'Five Hills', High Bannerdown, Bath BA1 7JY); Mrs Eleanor Catherine for the line drawings and Mrs Valerie Price for the paintings which illustrate and enhance this book, also David Henderson and Caroline Minnis for the invaluable technical maps.

The encouragement of Mr Geoffrey Scoble must not be overlooked. It was his great interest in Hebe for Cornish gardens that culminated in the forming of the Hebe Society and stimulated me to go on with the book.

Thank you to Miss Judith Mills for taking some of the burden of typing the manuscript and, above all, I would like to thank my wife, Diana, who has helped with the reading and correction of the text and has learned to live with the other Goddess in my life.

D.C.

Foreword

Alfred Russell Wallace, the famous nineteenth-century naturalist, once referred to New Zealand as the anomalous isles. Certainly, this fragment of Gondwanaland, the ancient southern continent, cast adrift in the South Pacific, contains many anomalies in both its plant and animal life, but nowhere are they more apparent than in the general lack of colour among its flowering plants.

White is the predominant colour and perhaps some 80 per cent of New Zealand's plants have flowers of white or yellow. There are no colourful meadows of wild flowers as in the northern hemisphere, nor are the shrublands as colourful as those of countries such as Australia or South Africa. In spite of that, many of the flowers have a beauty and perfection which is unrivalled.

In *Hebe*, New Zealand's largest genus of flowering plants, the flowers are predominantly white, mauve or purple, and yet how strange that this genus of some 80 species of subshrubs, shrubs and small trees should have so captured the hearts of gardeners that it is cultivated in temperate climates around the world. Particularly in Great Britain and France, numerous hybrids and cultivars have been produced and *Hebe* has achieved great popularity as a garden shrub. This has culminated in the formation of the Hebe Society, an honour not lightly accorded to any group of plants.

Originally all of the New Zealand species were classified under the genus *Veronica* but gradually some species have been split off into genera such as *Parahebe* and *Chionohebe*. *Parahebe* is becoming better known in cultivation and already several cultivars are being grown.

With the growing rise in the horticulture popularity of *Hebe* there has been an increasing demand, by keen gardeners, for a book on the subject. Until now none has existed and it is with pleasure and interest that I have read the manuscript of Douglas Chalk's *Hebes and Parahebes*. Of recent years it is the British who have led the way with the cultivation and breeding of Hebes, and so it is fitting that this book should have been written by an English horticulturist who has devoted so much time and effort to the cultivation and improvement of our knowledge of these plants. This is the first authoritative work dealing with these useful garden plants. It has been written for the professional and amateur horticulturist alike, and will do a great deal towards helping to correct the confusion which currently exists, particularly with the cultivars. I commend this book to all who have an interest in these beautiful and fascinating plants.

L.J. Metcalf,
Invercargill,
New Zealand

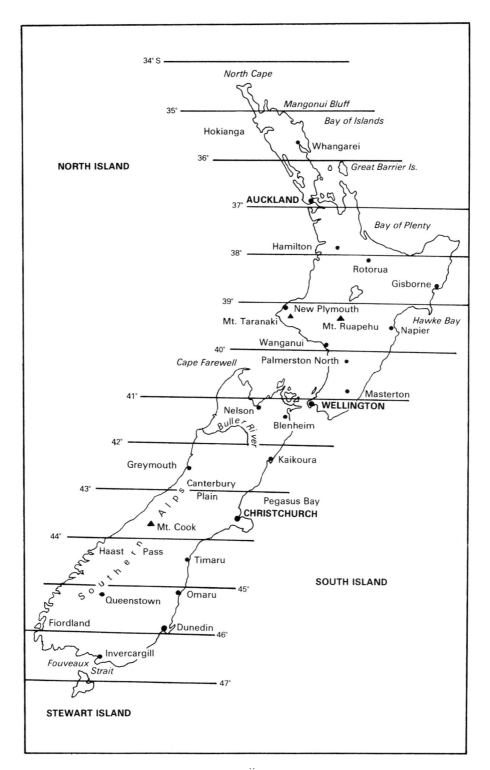

34° S ——— North Cape

Mangonui Bluff

35° ——— Bay of Islands

Hokianga

Whangarei

NORTH ISLAND

36° ——— ◊ Great Barrier Is.

37° — **AUCKLAND**

Bay of Plenty

38° — Hamilton •

Rotorua •

Gisborne •

39° — • New Plymouth
Mt. Taranaki ▲ ▲ Mt. Ruapehu   Hawke Bay
                                Napier •

40° — Wanganui •
Palmerston North •

Cape Farewell

41° — Masterton •
Nelson • **WELLINGTON**
• Blenheim

Buller River

42° —
Kaikoura •

Greymouth •
Canterbury
Plain

43° —
Pegasus Bay
Southern Alps
CHRISTCHURCH

▲ Mt. Cook

44° —
Haast Pass
Timaru •

45° — Omaru •
Queenstown •   **SOUTH ISLAND**

Fiordland
Dunedin •

46° —
Invercargill •

*Fouveaux
Strait*

47° —

STEWART ISLAND

New Zealand lies in the southern Pacific Ocean about 1,000 miles (1,610 km) south east of Australia and about 1,100 miles (1,760 km) south of Fiji and consists of two larger Islands and one smaller Island.

North Island — 44,200 sq miles (114,500 sq km) in area. Seventy-three per cent of the population live on this Island, which includes Auckland (population 769,560), with the international airport, and Wellington (population 321,000) the capital. Hamilton, Palmerston North, Napier and Tauranga are towns and cities with populations over 50,000. Average rainfall is 50–60 in (127–152 cm) and average sunshine 1,900 hours per year.

South Island — 58,200 sq miles (150,700 sq km) in area, with a continuous chain of mountains down the western side. Twenty-seven per cent of the population inhabit this Island. Christchurch (population 289,000) on the east coast is the largest city; other major cities are Dunedin (107,445 population), Nelson and Invercargill which have populations over 43,000. Average rainfall is very variable, from 28–100 in (71–254 cm), depending on locatoin. Average sunshine 1,950 hours; Nelson is the sunniest with over 2,400 hours.

Stewart Island — 656 sq miles (1,700 sq km) in area, 15 miles (25 km) due south of South Island across the windy Fouveaux Strait. The Island is 40 miles (65 km) from north to south and about 25 miles (40 km) across. The population is 450 and the main settlement is Oban; nearby is the airstrip and the harbour of Halfmoon Bay. Mt. Anglem 3,215 ft (980 m) dominates the north and Mt. Allen 2,460 ft (749 m) the south of the Island. Although the Maori name of Rakiura means 'heavenly glow', this so-called peaceful, bush-clad Island is dominated by wind and sea.

Total Population of New Zealand — 3,200,000 including 280,000 Maoris. The distance from North Cape, the equator end of North Island to the Fouveaux Strait, the Antarctic end of South Island is 1,055 miles (1,697 km).

1.1 Map of the three main Islands of New Zealand

HEBES
AND PARAHEBES

1

New Zealand

'A green and temperate land'

To understand the growing of Hebes in the northern hemisphere, where the seasons are in direct reverse to those in the southern hemispheres — which are spring from September to November, summer from December to February, autumn from March to May and winter from June to August — it might be helpful to learn a little about this green and temperate land of Aotearoa, the Long White Cloud, as it was called by the Polynesian race of Maoris, who landed and settled in the thirteenth century. The Dutch navigator, Abel Tasman, arrived in 1642 followed by the English navigator and explorer, Captain James Cook, who circumnavigated the three Islands in 1769, first landing at Poverty Bay. On his ship were the botanists Joseph Banks and Daniel Solander, who made records of the native plants growing in Poverty Bay, Queen Charlotte Sound and other localities where they landed.

What the botanists found was that most native trees and shrubs were evergreen with white flowers predominating. This is so with *Hebe*, the largest genus of native New Zealand plants, where about 80 of the 100 known species are found in the wild. The remaining 20 species are from Tasmania, South East Australia, Papua New Guinea, Chile, Tierra del Fuego and the Falkland Islands.

New Zealand lies in the Southern Pacific Ocean and consists of three main Islands — North Island, South Island and Stewart Island — with many smaller offshore islands. The territory lies between latitudes 34° and 47° south, whereas Britain, on the other hand, lies between latitudes 50° and 60° north. This does not imply that all New Zealand plants are not fully hardy in Britain. Hebes grow in the wild, from the sea shore to 9,000 ft (2,700 m) up in the mountains, which gives a widely varying climate. The evergreen Parahebes, previously included in Veronica, are found by streams or riversides, fell field and on mountain screes up to 4,500 ft (1,370 m) above sea level. The whipcord or conifer like Hebes are found mainly on the drier sides of the Southern Alps or other mountain ranges, amongst tussock grass and moist scrubland or in volcanic scree and rocks. What is not always realised is that three-quarters of the land in New Zealand stands more than 660 ft (200 m) above sea level and no part is more than 70 miles (113 km) from the coast. The total distance from North Cape in the sub-tropical north of the North Island to temperate Bluff on Fouveaux Strait or the south of South Island is 1,055 miles (1,697 km). Antarctica is a further 1,434 miles (2,308 km) south.

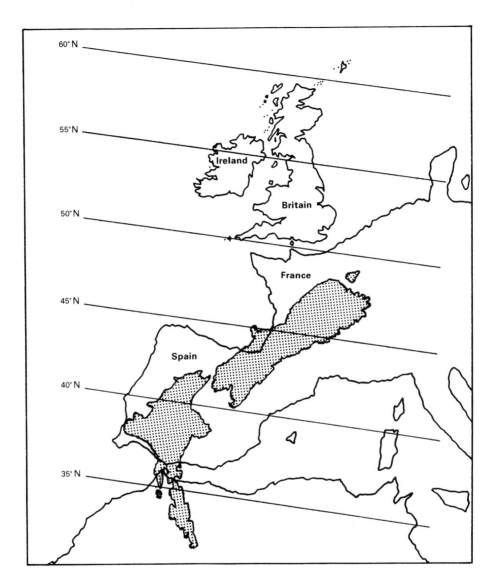

1.2 *Map of New Zealand inverted, to show how it fits into Europe in the same latitudes in the northern hemisphere*

Rainfall in New Zealand

Rainfall in many parts of New Zealand is spread over the whole year, without noticeable times when it can be drier, as in Britain. Average yearly rainfall is usually higher on the western side of both main Islands at between 40–50 in (102–127 cm), but in the South Island on the western side of the Southern Alps rainfall can be up to 100 in (254 cm) and in

Fiordland up to 300 in (762 cm). In contrast, on the eastern side, Napier in North Island has 31 in (79 cm) whereas Christchurch and Dunedin in South Island have 26–30 in (66–76 cm) of rain, and Alexandra in Central Otago has only 10–15 in (25–38 cm)! It is along the drier eastern coast that long summer droughts are likely to occur, and they are not uncommon. In North Island, the Poverty Bay and Hawke Bay areas can be affected and in South Island, Marlborough and Canterbury areas. East Otago can be affected by summer and winter droughts.

Over the rest of New Zealand, with a higher and more evenly spread annual rainfall, it is natural for plants and shrubs to be more surface rooting, so when growing Hebes in drier areas, it is wise to encourage deeper rooting and being prepared to water and mulch during dry periods and drought. In hot weather water evaporates rapidly, so water Hebes in the evenings or early mornings.

Mountains can be wetter than other places, but if there is rapid soil drainage and water loss through wind and high evaporation many plants, Hebe among these, have to be drought tolerant, so some knowledge of where a plant grows naturally can be helpful, when looking for plants to tolerate the soil and other conditions of your garden.

Wind Chill Factor

Britain is not only affected, as far as weather is concerned, by the warmer wetter winds from the west, but also by the drier colder winds from land masses to the east and north. On the other hand, New Zealand, with its long narrow islands across the path of the encircling wetter, westerly air stream of the southern hemisphere, with no colder drier winds from the east, is a rather windy country and most native evergreen shrubs have developed resistance to these winds.

In Britain, it is not only the air temperature that makes the weather feel cold, but the wind also plays a part and what is known as the *chill factor* is capable of making the air feel colder than the thermometer may be recording. The more the wind increases and the air temperature drops, the more noticeable the chilling effect becomes. As a rough guide, temperature drops 1°F for every 1 mph increase of wind speed (or subtract 1°C from the recorded temperature for every 3 km/h increase of wind speed). For example — with a temperature of 45°F (7.2°C) and a wind speed of 15 mph (24 km/h) the temperature would give the feel of 30°F (−1°C). The wind chill chart shows better the chilling effect the wind can have, especially a cold northerly or easterly wind.

Wind Chill Chart

Temperature		5 mph (8 km/h)		10 mph (16 km/h)		15 mph (24 km/h)		20 mph (32 km/h)		30 mph (48.2 km/h)	
°F	°C	°F	°C	°F	°C	°F	°C	°F	°C	°F	°C
30	−1.1	27	−2.8	16	−8.9	11	−11.7	3	−16.1	−2	−18.9
20	−6.7	16	−8.9	2	−16.7	−6	−21.1	−9	−22.8	−18	−27.8
10	−12.2	7	−13.9	−9	−22.8	−18	−27.8	−24	−31.1	−33	−36.1
0	−17.8	−6	−21.1	−22	−30.0	−33	−36.1	−40	−40.0	−49	−45.0
−10	−23.3	−15	−26.1	−31	−35.0	−45	−42.8	−52	−47.0	−63	−53.9
−15	−26.1	−20	−28.9	−38	−38.9	−51	−46.0	−60	−52.0	−70	−62.6

This explains why it is as well to protect plants against cold east and north winds. By slowing these winds, the damage from chilling can be minimised. Winds can also cause damage by their strength. In Britain, coastal storms cause damage to larger leaved trees and shrubs by blowing off leaves, twigs and even branches. The native New Zealand evergreen shrubs, including Hebes, being resistant to the wind, suffer only minimal damage in strong winds.

Frosts and Frost Damage

Frost is another weather problem that has to be considered and again it is important to understand there are two main causes of frost in Britain. The first cause is a mass of cold polar air moving over the country and causing an overall lowering of the temperature. This movement of air can occur not only in the winter, but even in the early spring, after plant growth has started. The second cause is due to loss of temperature on still clear nights, when there is no cloud to stop the loss of heat from the soil. This is known as a *radiation frost*. During a sunny day the soil is warmed by the sun, but the air is not appreciably warmed, being transparent to the heat rays. At night fall the air nearest the ground is warmest, due to conduction of heat from the soil and the air gradually gets colder the further upward one goes. The air nearest the ground gets heavier as it cools and has no tendency to move. If the night is long then the loss of heat may be suffi- cient for the temperature to fall below freezing point and the moisture in the colder layer of air can be deposited as *ground frost*. Formation of cloud can slow down the loss of heat radiation from the ground. Winds getting up can also help in moving this heavier air, which tends to build up on flat, level ground; but where the ground slopes, the tendency is for the colder air to move down the slope to lower levels, creating pockets of frost. Hedges, walls or fences can hold up this down hill movement, so by creating gaps in the obstruction, the frost can be encouraged to flow and not build up and cause damage to those plants trapped in the frost build up.

Both types of frost may happen simultaneously; if this does happen, then the fall in temperature can be very rapid and severe.

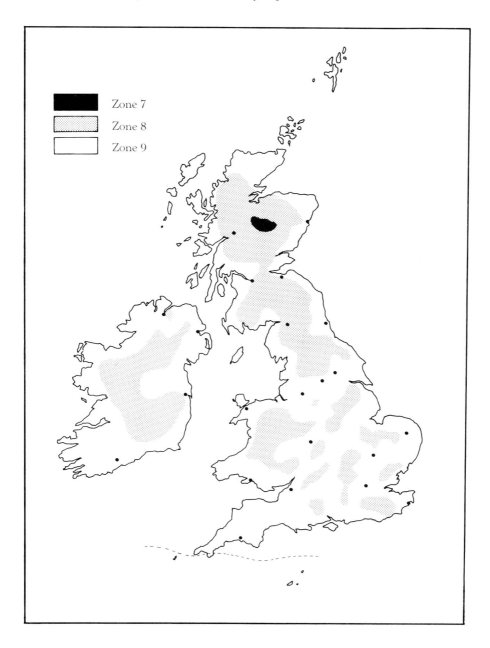

1.3 Zone map of British Isles

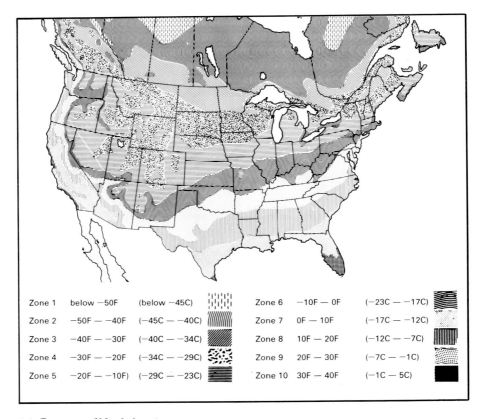

Zone 1	below −50F	(below −45C)		Zone 6	−10F — 0F	(−23C — −17C)	
Zone 2	−50F — −40F	(−45C — −40C)		Zone 7	0F — 10F	(−17C — −12C)	
Zone 3	−40F — −30F	(−40C — −34C)		Zone 8	10F — 20F	(−12C — −7C)	
Zone 4	−30F — −20F	(−34C — −29C)		Zone 9	20F — 30F	(−7C — −1C)	
Zone 5	−20F — −10F)	(−29C — −23C)		Zone 10	30F — 40F	(−1C — 5C)	

1.4 Zone map of North America

In New Zealand ground frost may occur in most parts from the sub-tropical north to the temperate south, but duration is usually shorter than in Britain. The windy conditions, too, help in reducing the effects of the build up of colder air.

Cold Hardiness and Zones

As there are many factors involved, it is not possible to say what is the lowest temperature any particular Hebe will stand. Zone hardiness figures can only be a guide.

The cold hardiness of shrubs was studied by the Arnold Arboretum for North America and they worked out a zonal system of classification, but this has now been superseded as shown on the accompanying United States Department of Agriculture (USDA) hardiness zone maps of Great Britain and North America (Figures 1.3 and 1.4).

Shrubs that withstand low temperature may have difficulty in living in high temperatures and the same is true the other way around. An evergreen shrub that is hardy by the sea, may be killed by cold winds and frost away from the coast at 500 ft (152 m) or even less. There are frost pockets within the zones, so that a shrub hardy in Zone 9 may be desiccated or severely damaged in a frost pocket. In the lists of Hebes and Parahebes, only those numbers which concern the British Isles have been used, namely Zones 7–10, but many of those Hebes within Zone 7 can possibly survive in Zone 6. Some of those in Zone 10 may survive in protected sites in Zone 9.

It is wise to assess the site or garden first, then choose Hebes that you think will tolerate and grow in the conditions.

1.5 Hebe odora *growing at 2,000 ft (610 m) on Bald Hill, Otautau, South Island, New Zealand*

2
What are Hebes and Parahebes?

In Britain, gardeners have been reluctant to use Hebe, the Goddess of Youth's name, for a genus of plants which are still referred to as shrubby Veronicas. Possibly because most of the Hebes were introduced into Britain as Veronicas. The first shrubby Veronica to arrive was *V.elliptica* in 1776 from the Falkland Islands followed by *V.diosmifolia* and *V.speciosa* in 1835 from New Zealand.

The name Hebe was suggested as long ago as 1789, for these shrubby evergreen plants from the southern hemisphere, which have proved to be both decorative and useful. F.W. Pennell revived the name Hebe in 1921, but it was not till 1926, following the submission to the New Zealand Institute (now the Royal Society of New Zealand), of a paper on Hebe by Doctors L. Cockayne and H.H. Allan pointing out the significant differences between Hebe and Veronica, was it agreed in New Zealand that Hebe should become a separate genus. As late as 1952, in the RHS *Dictionary of Gardening*, it was still being recommended that Hebes should still be called Veronicas. Hebe was finally recognised in 1985, with the setting up of the Hebe Society in London, Britain, after nearly 40 years, fell into line with New Zealand over the naming of this genus.

In New Zealand at the present time more species than varieties and cultivars are being grown, whereas in Britain the reverse is the case, with many more cultivars than species. France, too, has produced several good cultivars, which explains cultivar names of *Hebe speciosa* hybrids like *H.*'La Seduisante' and *H.* 'Simon Delaux'. Although it is cultivars that are coming forward today, it could be that in the remoter parts of New Zealand there are Hebe species still to be discovered, but these will be introduced under their rightful name of Hebe. It is very unlikely that a new species may be found; more likely is that on critical examination a Hebe of uncertain origin may be found to be a true species.

What are the differences that distinguish Hebe from Veronica? Hebes are all evergreen shrubs, whereas most Veronicas are deciduous and herbaceous. With Hebes the growing points at the ends of the shoots are always covered by leaves. This is helpful in coastal districts, where the protected growing points are less likely to be damaged by the strong, salt laden winds, blowing off the sea. Hebes growing by the sea are usually upright and healthy, whereas trees and shrubs, with their seaward buds being constantly damaged by the winds, tend to grow one sided and away from the sea.

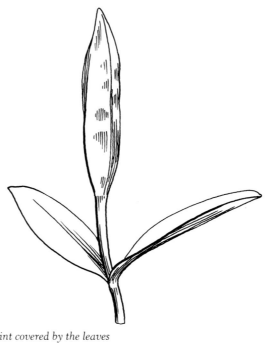

2.1 Hebe: growing point covered by the leaves

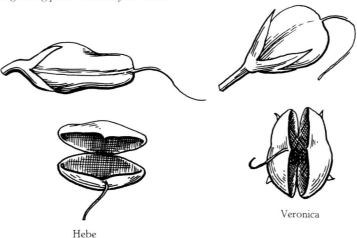

Veronica

Hebe

2.2 How the seed pods split: Hebe horizontally, Veronica vertically

Another difference that can be seen is the way the seed pods split, when ripe. In Veronicas the splitting is vertical, whereas in Hebe and Parahebe the splitting is horizontal across the seed pod (see Figure 2.2). In Parahebe the capsule is also laterally compressed.

The final difference can not be seen, but should be mentioned. It concerns the number of chromosomes that are in the plant cells. In

Veronica the counts are lower than the counts of chromosomes in the plant cells of Hebe and Parahebe.

Whipcord Hebes

The whipcord Hebes are a unique group of 14 species, with a few varieties and cultivars. The whipcords are all native of the mountains and uplands of New Zealand, growing on terraces, along river flats and in wet tussock grass and scrubland from 2,000–5,000 ft (600–1,500 m). Hence many are useful for rock and scree gardens, taking the place of conifers. *Hebe cupressoides*, a dense, much branched shrub, is easily mistaken for a conifer, with its glaucous green leaves and cypress like appearance.

The whipcord Hebes are like conifers in another respect, they also produce juvenile or young foliage, with small more rounded leaves, as distinct from the adult foliage with its stalkless, short leaves, often pressed and overlapping the thin 'whipcord like' branches. This prevents excess loss of transpiration or moisture in the strong winds on the mountains. Most whipcords are slow growing due to where and how they grow.

For those conifer orientated gardeners, this group of starry flowered Hebes is worth exploring and will prove fascinating and rewarding. Amongst the whipcords, the following have proved popular in the garden: *H.cupressoides* 'Boughton Dome' (18 in/45 cm), *H.*'Edinensis' (9–12 in/ 22–30 cm), *H.laingii* (6–8 in/15–20 cm), *H.ochracea* or its cultivar 'James Stirling' (42 in/105 cm) and *H.propinqua* (up to 36 in/90 cm) — the lower growing forms are often sold as *H.propinqua minor*.

Parahebes

The *Parahebes* (para = like) are distinguished from Veronicas in being evergreen, prostrate or decumbent subshrubs with woody bases to their stems. The flowers are often veined and usually speedwell or saucer like, but some can be more funnel shaped. There are 11 species all within New Zealand and in the wild can be found on cliffs and rocky places, from lowlands to mountainsides, as well as along streamsides, where they grow in the sands and silts deposited in the rock crevices. There is noticeable variation in some of the species and this seems to be linked with the climatic nature of their habitat, which affects the leaf size and growth.

The Parahebes were included in Veronica and arrived in Britain from New Zealand from 1876 onwards. In 1926 they joined Hebes, and were parted from the Veronicas, but it was not until 1944 that they became a genus in their own right, as Parahebes. As well as species there are a small number of varieties and cultivars and most are hardy.

Hebe, Parahebe and Veronica all belong to the family Scrophulariacae, which embraces about 220 genera of herbs, subshrubs, shrubs and trees, many with beautiful flowers and including such well known garden plants as Antirrhinum, Foxglove, Mimulus, Nemesia, Penstemon and Verbascum (Mullein).

11

3
The features of Hebes

Hebes are worthy of a place in any garden, as they can provide interest the year round in many ways from colour and shape of flowers and leaves, colour of stems, to their habit of growth. The shrubby Hebes are mostly rounded in outline and grow in height from a few inches (centimetres) to 13 ft (4 m), while some Hebes are low growing and cover ground and rocks. The whipcord Hebes are conifer like, giving a spiky effect, with the small leaves often clasped around the stem.

To expand on these interests that Hebes provide for the gardener and flower arranger, let us look at them in more detail.

Shape and Texture of Leaves

Leaves of Hebe come in a variety of shapes from ovate or oval to elliptical, from linear to lanceolate, and from oblong to whipcord. Leaves can vary in size from an ⅛ in (3 mm) to 6 in (150 mm) in length and from ¼ in (6 mm) to 2 in (50 mm) in width. On the other hand the actual leaves of whipcords can be as small as ¹⁄₃₂ in (0.79 mm) in length and width. In texture, leaves can vary from thin to leathery and thick.

Colour of Leaves

Not only are there mid green leaves, but other interesting colours as well, as shown by the following examples:

Yellow green	— *H.rakaiensis*
Gold tipped	— *H.odora* 'New Zealand Gold'
Dark green and glossy	— *H.vernicosa* and *H.odora* 'Wintergreen'
Reddish green	— *H.*'La Seduisante', *H.*'Simon Delaux', *H.speciosa*
Bronzy green or grey	— *H.*'Caledonia', *H.*'Colwall', *H.*'County Park'
Bronze or deep bronze	— *H.*'Amy', *H.*'Eversley Seedling', *H.*'Mrs Winder', *H.*'Purple Queen'
Old gold	— *H.ochracea*, *H.hectori*, *H.armstrongii* (whipcords)
Greeny grey	— *H.cupressoides* (whipcord)

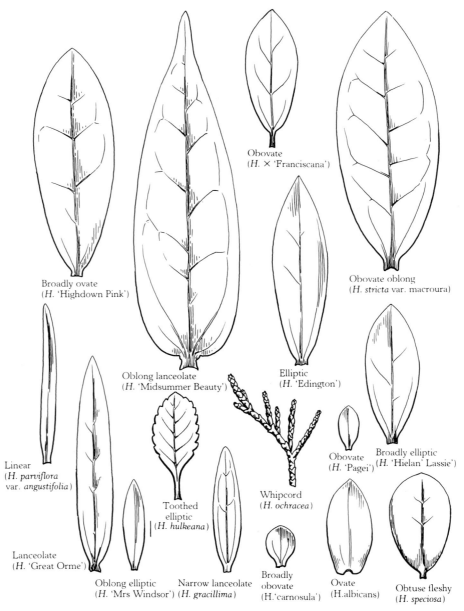

Obovate
(H. × 'Franciscana')

Broadly ovate
(H. 'Highdown Pink')

Obovate oblong
(H. stricta var. macroura)

Oblong lanceolate
(H. 'Midsummer Beauty')

Elliptic
(H. 'Edington')

Linear
(H. parviflora
var. angustifolia)

Broadly elliptic
(H. 'Hielan' Lassie')

Obovate
(H. 'Pagei')

Toothed
elliptic
(H. hulkeana)

Whipcord
(H. ochracea)

Lanceolate
(H. 'Great Orme')

Oblong elliptic
(H. 'Mrs Windsor')

Narrow lanceolate
(H. gracillima)

Broadly
obovate
(H. 'carnosula')

Ovate
(H. albicans)

Obtuse fleshy
(H. speciosa)

3.1 Differing leaf shapes of Hebes

Grey and grey green — *H. albicans, H. 'Carnosula', H. colensoi* var. *glauca, H. 'Pagei', H. 'Pewter Dome', H. pinguifolia, H. pimeleoides* var. *glauco-caerulea, H. 'Wingletye'*

14

There are also Hebes with leaves with more than one colour or variegated:

Cream and green	— *H.*'Andersonii Variegata', *H.*'Andersonii Anne Pimm', *H.glaucophylla* 'Variegata' (*H.*'Darwiniana')
Yellow and green	— *H.*'Andersonni Aurea', *H.*'Franciscana Variegata'
Cream, green and plum	— *H.*'Purple Tips' ('La Seduisante'), *H.*'Lopen' (sport from 'Midsummer Beauty')

Colour of leaves can vary with the time of year: bronze leaves can become more green during summer, whereas some yellow green leaves become more yellow in winter. Colour can be more intense in sun than in shade, especially with variegated leaved cultivars. Soil depth, type and fertility can also have its effect on leaf colour. Climate, too, can affect growth and with it, leaf colour. Hebes in New Zealand generally grow in areas of higher rainfall than in Britain. In the south west of Britain, the higher humidity of the coastal districts favours Hebes; leaves are not damaged by salt spray or salt laden winds, whereas the very cold, piercing north or east winds can desiccate, burn or kill. There is a saying that the smaller the leaves the greater the hardiness, and there is some truth in it as far as Hebe is concerned.

Leaf bud Sinus and Domatia

Leaf features can also be used as an aid to identification. Many Hebes have a sinus at the base of the pair of leaves covering the growing point. Look at right angles to the way the leaves will next open and you will find a recess or sinus; its shape, be it narrow or long or round, is used as an aid to identification of both Hebe species and cultivars. Figure 3.2 shows more clearly what to observe.

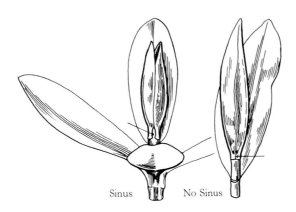

Sinus   No Sinus

3.2 The sinus, if present, is found at the base of the pair of leaves covering the growing point

15

The other feature that can be mentioned is the presence of domatia on the under surface of the leaves of *Hebe townsonii*. No other species or variety carries these short, oblique pits or domatia along each side of the leaf and close to the margins, as shown in Figure 3.3. This makes *Hebe townsonii* the easiest Hebe to identify.

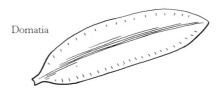

Domatia

3.3 Domatia or pits on the underside of Hebe townsonii

Colour of Stems

Like the leaves, there are not only green stems but other colours as well. Most of the colour is in the young stems or branchlets; as the stems age they may become grey, grey brown or light brown or even remain green or greeny brown.

Yellow or yellow green	— *H.ochracea, H.odora* 'New Zealand Gold', *H.salicifolia*
Grey or grey green	— *H.albicans, H. colensoi* var *glauca, H.cupressoides*
Bronzy green	— *H.*'Pewter Dome', *H.rakaiensis, H.vernicosa*
Light bronze or brown	— *H.*'Bowles' Variety', *H.*'Carnosula', *H.*'Primley Gem'
Bronze or deep brown	— *H.*'Autumn Glory', *H.*'Edington', *H.*'Mrs Winder'
Red brown	— *H.*'Caledonia', *H.*'Eversley Seedling', *H.*'Warleyensis'

Some stems, and in some cases margins of the leaves, as in *Hebe gibbsii*, have short hairs, which give a pubescent or downy look to the stem or leaf.

Times of Flowering

May to June is the main flowering period for many of the lower growing Hebes and whipcord Hebes. The medium and taller growing Hebes, including those with larger leaves, tend to flower from July to September in Britain. Naturally there are exceptions, like *Hebe* 'Eversley Seedling', which flowers several times during the year and is perhaps the longest flowering Hebe. By noting the flowering times, it is possible to have Hebes in flower over much of the year.

Colour of Flowers

The two commonest flower colours are white and mauve; add blue, purple and violet to these two colours and you have the range of colours of the hardiest Hebes. By using *Hebe speciosa*, which comes from the sub-tropical north east coast of New Zealand's North Island, it has been possible to produce the more exotic coloured hybrids, with flower colours which include beetroot purple, carmine and mid to deep pink and purple. *Hebe speciosa* is possibly one parent of *Hebe* 'Carnea', a spontaneous hybrid that arose in a New Zealand garden and which in turn has given rise to a number of pink hybrids of varying heights. The flowers of *H*.'Carnea' and it hybrids lighten as they age, becoming almost white, so giving a bicolour effect to the spikes of flower. This happens, too, with some *Hebe speciosa* hybrids and some other cultivars.

Stamen anthers are often coloured mauve, purple or bronze and these also add colour to the flowers.

Types of Flowers

In Hebe, the flowers are sometimes displayed as single flowers on a stem, but are mostly displayed as spikes of flowers, either short with a few

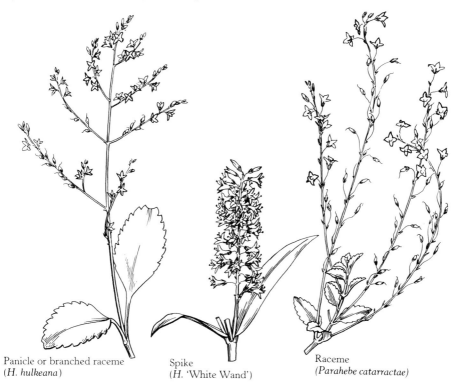

Panicle or branched raceme
(*H. hulkeana*)

Spike
(*H.* 'White Wand')

Raceme
(*Parahebe catarractae*)

3.4 Hebe and Parahebe: types of flower — panicle, spike and raceme

flowers or long with many flowers. In *Hebe hulkeana* and its hybrids *H.*'Fairfieldii' and *H.*'Hagley Park' (*H.*'Hagleyensis') the flowers are displayed in a branched raceme or panicle.

In Parahebes, the flowers are displayed in axillary racemes of varying length; up to 9 in (22.5 cm) in length in *Parahebe catarractae*. Parahebe flowers, too, vary in size up to ½ in (12 mm) in diameter and in shape from flat to saucer shaped like speedwell flowers. Flower colours are white, veined pink, mauve and purple.

Parahebes make ideal plants for the rock garden, as they are summer and autumn flowering. They are useful, too, for sinks and troughs.

HEBE REFERENCE TABLE — a quick reference and guide to those Hebes and Parahebes mentioned under the Features of Hebes and Parahebes; for fuller details see the alphabetical Lists of Hebe and Parahebe species and cultivars (Chapters 8 and 10). The page number is given after each name, thus (42). * = Half hardy or tender.

Species or Cultivar	Height (in)	(cm)	Flower Colour	Leaf Colour	Time of Flowering
H.albicans (48)	24	60	white	grey green	summer
H.'Amy' (50)	54	137	violet	dark bronze	summer
H.'Andersonii Anne Pimm' (51)	48	120	pinky purple	cream/green	summer
H.'Andersonii Aurea' (51)	60	150	light violet	yellow/green	summer
H.'Andersonii variegata' (51)	60	150	light violet	cream/green	summer
H.armstrongii (52)	36	90	white	greeny yellow	May–June
H.'Autumn Glory' (53)	30	75	violet	dark green	Aug.–Sept.
H.'Bowles' Variety' (59)	18	45	mauvy blue	mid green	June onwards
H.'Caledonia' (61)	18	45	violet	green, red edge	late May–Sept.
H.'Carnea' (62)	48	120	rosy purple	mid green	summer
H.'Carnosula' (62)	16	40	white	grey green	June
H.colensoi var. glauca (65)	18	45	white	grey green	summer
H.'Colwall' (65)	12	30	cyclamen purple	dark green	late May–June
H.'County Park' (66)	8	20	violet	grey green	June–July
H.cupressoides (67)	54	137	bluish purple	greeny grey	May–June
H.'Edington' (73)	42	105	bright purple	dark green	late May/Sept.
H.'Eversley Seedling' (76)	42	105	amethyst purple	green/red brown	May/autumn
H.'Fairfieldii' (76)	12	30	lavender violet	dark green	early summer
H.'Franciscana Variegata' (79)	36	90	pinky purple	yellow/green	summer
H.gibbsii (80)	12	30	white	grey green	May/June
H.glaucophylla 'Variegata' (80)	42	105	lilac	grey green/cream	summer
H.'Hagley Park' (84)	16	40	rosy purple	mid green	end of May/June

Quick Reference continued:

Species or Cultivar	Height (in)	(cm)	Flower Colour	Leaf Colour	Time of Flowering
H.hectori (85)	30	75	white	yellow brown	summer
*H.hulkeana (87)	24	60	lavender	dark green	late May
*H.'La Seduisante' (92)	54	137	violet purple	dark green	summer
*H.'Lopen' (95)	54	137	lilac purple	green, yellow and cream	summer
H.'Mrs Winder' (101)	36	90	violet	dark green	late summer
H.ochracea (102)	42	105	white	olive green	May–June
H.odora 'New Zealand Gold' (103)	42	105	white	dark green	summer
H.odora 'Wintergreen' (104)	42	105	white	mid green	summer
H.'Pagei' (104)	4	10	pearly white	grey	May
H.'Pewter Dome' (107)	15	37	white	grey	May/June
H.pimeleoides var. *glaucocaerulea* (108)	12	30	bluish purple	yellowish/reddish	summer
H.pinguifolia (109)	9	22	white	grey green	June
H.'Primley Gem' (111)	30	75	mauvy blue	dark green	summer
*H.'Purple Queen' (113)	54	137	violet purple	dark green, bronze below	summer
*H.'Purple Tips' (113)	48	120	violet purple	grey green/cream	summer
H.rakaiensis (114)	24	60	white	apple green	late May
H.salicifolia (117)	60	150	white	mid green	July/Aug.
*H.'Simon Delaux' (118)	48	120	crimson	dark green	late summer
*H.speciosa (119)	54	135	beetroot purple	dark green	summer/ autumn
H.townsonii (123)	42	105	white	bright green	April/May
H.vernicosa (125)	15	37	pale lavender	lustrous green	May
H.'Warleyensis' (127)	30	75	methyl violet	glossy green	summer/ autumn
*H.'Warley Pink' (128)	60	150	mid/deep pink	mid green	summer
H.'Wingletye' (130)	6	15	amethyst	grey	early summer
P.catarractae (133)	8	20	veined purple	mid/dark green	summer
P.catarractae 'Delight' (134)	8	20	veined heliotrope, purple eye	mid green	summer
P.linifolia 'Blue Skies' (135)	6	15	lavender, purple eye	dark green	summer

4
Growing Hebes and Parahebes

Loamy soils, well drained and of good depth are the ideal; but how many soils are ideal? Many New Zealand soils are stony and gravelly yet Hebes survive and flourish, because of the higher rainfall of the area. Hebes are surface rooting and dislike drought conditions, so if growing Hebes on sandy or gravelly soils, watering is necessary in dry periods.

Hebes and Parahebes are very tolerant and will grow ideally in soils ranging from slightly acid (pH 6.0) to slightly alkaline (pH 7.5), but they will equally thrive in more acid or alkaline soils.

Organic matter is the key to growing Hebes in soils that are not ideal. In sandy, open soils organic matter such as compost, leaf mould, peat or rotted manure is needed to retain moisture and prevent drying out, whereas in heavier soils such as clays, organic matter of a coarser nature is needed to provide drainage. Being evergreen, Hebes will certainly suffer in waterlogged or wet soils in winter. Organic matter also holds any fertilisers applied to open soils and prevents their being washed through. Balanced fertilisers are to be preferred as the very soft growth produced by nitrogeneous fertilisers can be more readily damaged by winds and frosts, especially on the larger leaved Hebes.

The importance of mulching in spring to prevent drying out of the soil and in autumn to limit frost penetration is a necessary part of successful cultivation. Gardeners are always looking to increase the range of plants they grow, so an understanding of the climatic factors that affect the well being of plants can only be helpful. The two factors that most affect gardeners are frost and wind, so let us look at them in more detail.

Frost

Hebes and Parahebes, being evergreen, are not dormant through the winter, therefore the roots need to extract water from the soil. If the ground is frozen solid, water can not be drawn up and the leaves suffer and can even collapse and die from water shortage. Root damage can occur through the expansion and contraction (freezing and thawing) of the soil. The rapid thaw of snow cover can also create problems with waterlogging of the soil and the resultant asphixiation of the roots. Young, soft tissue is usually more susceptible to damage than older, more mature leaves and stems. A mild autumn followed by a sudden, severe cold spell

21

or a very severe frost can be very damaging, as the plants are starting to grow again after a cold period.

If the fall in temperature is slow, ice crystals formed in the intercellular spaces will cause little damage provided the thaw is equally slow. A rapid thaw may cause the intercellular spaces to flood and the cells can die through lack of air, before the water can be absorbed. A rapid fall in temperature can cause the water in the cells to freeze. With freezing comes the expansion of the cells and these in consequence can burst and die. Rapid freezing can also cause bark splitting in shrubby plants and trees.

The countering of frost damage depends on the stage and kind of growth, the nature of the plant, the conditions under which it is growing, the slowing of the speed of freezing and, most important, the slowing of the speed of thawing. Where the protective hedge is not high enough or frost resistant shrubs are not protecting Hebes from cold north or east winds, loosely wrapping exposed bushes in 'Rokolene' or fairly fine mesh netting, is a temporary measure when cold spells are forecast.

Wind

Gentle breezes help transpiration, remove stagnant air and with it any pollutants, humid air and, in addition, assist in the pollination of flowers by helping the flight of pollinating insects and bees. Strong winds and gales on the other hand can cause damage by bruising and tearing or even breaking flowers, leaves, twigs and branches of shrubs and trees. Strong winds can also carry dust, pollutants from industry and salt sea spray.

Wind direction can be a factor in deciding where and what we plant. In Britain, the warmer winds come usually from the south west and west, whereas the colder winds come from the north or east or from the continent or Europe. Increasing wind run means increasing transpiration and when this occurs with piercing cold, easterly winds, then leaves can be desiccated and dried out by having all the moisture dragged from them causing burning or even death. The larger the leaves the greater the damage from the wind.

These two factors highlight the need in coastal or exposed positions, for shelter to be established first. Shelter is not only needed against the cold or strong winds, but also against the rising early morning sun to prevent the rapid thawing out of our choicer plants.

With this added knowledge it will now be possible to provide the climate to grow a wider range of plants. Augustus Smith did just this, when he created the famous Tresco Gardens on the Isle of Scilly. It is advisable, when moving to an unknown area, to explore thoroughly the local gardens, note the plants that are thriving and talk to the gardeners, before embarking on the creation of your own garden.

Soil Preparation, Planting and Mulching

The main operations in soil preparation can be summed up as follows.

Remove perennial weeds, such as dandelion, couch grass and dock. If these are few, they can be removed during digging; otherwise, apply a specific herbicide like glyphosate (for example 'Tumbleweed' or 'Round Up') and delay planting.

Encourage deeper rooting by breaking up the lower spit, whilst digging and working in organic matter, such as rotted manure or straw, leaves or compost. On light and open soils this organic matter will retain moisture and fertilisers that might have been leached away. With heavy and clay soils the organic matter acts in a different way: it opens up the soil and allows drainage of excess water and the entry of air. In both cases roots will tend to grow deeper in search of food and anchorage. Clay and heavy soils preparation should ideally be carried out in the autumn, whereas on open and light soils, work can be done within a few weeks of planting.

Planting ideally takes place in spring, after the severe frosts have gone, so that the plant can get well established before the winter comes.

When planting Hebes the following points are worth remembering:

(a) Water the pot or container prior to planting and before the removal of the container or pot. Plastic pots or bags slip off a moist rootball more easily, whereas they will stick and be difficult to remove from a dry rootball.

(b) Site preparation — if it is clay subsoil, then the site should be dug and prepared overall. If only holes are dug, the forking up of the soil or subsoil at the bottom of the hole will make a collecting point for water and the roots of the planted shrub can be waterlogged and killed in very rainy periods.

(c) Always take the hole out wider for easy working and deeper for forking into the bottom organic matter such as compost, leafmould or well rotted manure. If dry, water the bottom of the hole plentifully, so that there is water there for the roots to draw on.

(d) With the lower growing and the carpeting hardy Hebes and Para-hebes, plant normally with the soil level of the top of the rootball just below the surface. Taller Hebes, especially the large leaved and less hardy Hebes, can be planted about 2 in (5 cm) lower, so that there are at least four dormant buds below ground. In the event of the bushes being cut back by severe weather and frost, there are buds from which regrowth can take place.

(e) Do not break up the rootball when planting, only spread out any loose roots at the base. Work in a little peat or well rotted compost into the soil, as you fill in around the rootball. Firm evenly and sufficiently to prevent wind rocking of the shrub. Water well and allow the water to drain in.

(f) Apply 1–2 oz (28–56 g) of a balanced fertiliser, like 'Growmore', to the soil around the shrub, then level off the surface. The Hebe being surface rooting will benefit more this way than from fertiliser applied at the bottom of the hole.

(g) Apply a mulch, of sufficient depth to deter germination of annual weed seeds, of peat, forest bark, mushroom compost, or grass mowings provided the lawn has not been treated with a hormone type weedkiller. This mulch will help in preventing drying out and the over zealous gardener hoeing or forking around the bush and damaging or killing the surface roots.

It is useful to remember when choosing sites or planting Hebes, that Hebes with variegated or bronzed foliage should be planted in the sun, as this intensifies the colour. Many Hebes are equally at home in sunny or shady positions, but too shady a site can reduce and delay the flowering.

4.1 The deeper planting of less hardy Hebes

Planting Distances

There are no set planting distances for Hebes and Parahebes. Planting distances can vary with the habit of the plant; spreading plants may need to be wider apart than upright growing plants. Here are some suggested planting distances:

Carpeting Hebes and Parahebes	— up to 12 in (30 cm) apart
Hebes up to 18 in (45 cm) high	— 15–18 in (37–45 cm) apart
Hebes up to 36 in (90 cm) high	— 24 in (60 cm) apart
Hebes up to 48 in (120 cm) high	— 36 in (90 cm) apart
Taller growing Hebes	— 48 in (120 cm) apart

Shelter Belts and Coastal Planting

In open or exposed gardens, where there is a need for shelter, temporary protection could be provided by plastic netting, such as Rokolene or Netlon, until the plants are established. Where there is room, taller Hebes, such as *Hebe salicifolia*, *H.*'Miss E. Fittall', *H.*'Violet' or *H.*'Blush Wand', can be planted as a background screen. Allow your background Hebes to establish themselves and provide some protection, before planting the less hardy Hebes you are wanting to plant. Remember the background Hebes will need the same after planting temporary protection.

In coastal districts, the New Zealand *Hebe stricta* from the North Island and *Hebe dieffenbachii* from Chatham Islands grow well in spite of the strong winds. Other Hebes that grow by the sea are *Hebe* × 'Franciscana' and its parent *Hebe elliptica*, as well as the hybrids of *Hebe* × 'Franciscana' namely 'Blue Gem', 'Lavender Queen' and the lower growing *H.*× 'Franciscana Variegata'. The smaller leaved, slower growing *Hebe brachysiphon*, which is used for shelter hedges in the Isles of Scilly, should also be included. *Hebe speciosa* and its hybrids are grown in sheltered coastal districts.

Aftercare of the newly planted Hebes consists of regularly watering around and over the bushes in dry spells at either end of the day. Encourage bushy growth, especially of the larger leaved Hebes, by pinching out the growing points of any shoots tending to grow too long. Any straggly shoots should be pruned back to where there is a bud breaking or there is a growing shoot. Usually little pruning is needed by the carpeting Hebes and Parahebes, other than the removal of any straggling shoots and dead flowers.

a. Prune here to reduce
   length of side shoots

b. Prune back to growing side shoot
   to remove old terminal flowers

4.2 Aftercare: pruning side shoots and growing point

Following on from coastal planting is a query that often arises when trying to establish a shelter belt. 'Why do planted trees and shrubs get damaged or even blown over in gales, whilst native trees survive with minimal damage?'

The answer lies with the root system — native trees and shrubs arise from seed and therefore have a primary root system, often with tap root and anchor roots, to hold that tree or shrub against the elements. Trees and shrubs which have been vegetatively propagated have a secondary or adventitious root system, just fine roots to start with and no anchor or tap roots.

The New Zealand nurserymen, with their deeper wedge shaped 'root-rainer' propagation pots, encourage roots to go down rather than round and round as in seed tray or pot. These New Zealand plants, when planted out, respond quickly with the roots going down into the soil and establishing that tree or shrub.

For shelter belts in exposed or coastal plantings use seedlings. Get the shelter belt established first and growing, then when the shelter belt is giving protection, Hebes and other choicer shrubs can be planted.

Pruning Established Hebes

As pruning can confound some gardeners, let us say why we prune: first, for a natural shape, which means removal of straggly growths and correcting any irregular or one-sided growth; secondly, to encourage growth and flowering. By encouraging young wood the shrub's life and continuity of good flowering can be prolonged. Thirdly, for health, by removing any damaged, diseased or dead wood.

Being evergreen, the Hebe is living and not dormant in the winter months, and therefore, foliage and shoots can be damaged by wind and frost. If the damage is light, then it can be removed in April, when the weather is mild; whereas in the case of severe damage or dieback, it is better to wait until signs of growth appear, then cut back to where it is growing strongly. Make a clean cut across the stem, just above the growing bud. Cuts larger than 1 in (2.5 cm) across can be treated with a bituminous paint to keep out fungal spores. To keep a natural shape, vary the heights and lengths of cuts, so that the new shoots do not arise at the same level and give a crowded, unnatural appearance.

With the prostrate and spreading Hebes and Parahebes, there is little pruning needed, just the cutting back of the odd, straggling shoot to where there is a strong bud or shoot arising. Low, slow growing, narrow leaved and whipcord Hebes can be pruned in the same way. Carry out this pruning when the weather is mild, in April or August, but not in a drought period. Remember, when pruning in April, you could be removing the coming flowers from the early flowering Hebes, so be patient and wait till after flowering.

In the case of the larger leaved and taller growing Hebes, these are pruned as soon as they have flowered. The flowered shoots are pruned back to where the growth buds or shoots are appearing, in this way you will encourage better growth as well as better flowering in the next year. With Hebes that flower in autumn or winter, delay the pruning of the flowered shoots until April.

In well established or older bushes any reduction of height or spread should be gradual, carrying out the work over a period and not all at once. Always cut back to where there is a growing bud or shoot. Pare cuts smooth with a knife, if over 1 in (2.5 cm), and paint. With dead wood or diseased wood cut back to the main branch and do not leave a horn or hat peg to become infected. It is advised to wear strong gloves, as the wood can so easily tear the skin on the back of the hand. Dead Hebe wood is fairly tough, so you may have to use short arm loppers or a saw to remove it.

Pests and Diseases

Hebes suffer from few pests and diseases when growing out of doors. In the sheltered and coastal districts and the milder south west, of Britain fungal leaf spots (*Septoria* sp.) can be disfiguring to the larger leaved Hebes, in which case use a systemic fungicide like benomyl (Benlate) or a fungicide like Thiram. Under glass or in plastic structures downy mildew can sometimes be troublesome to some Hebes and especially the paniculate group, namely *Hebe hulkeana*, *H.*'Hagley Park' (*H.*'Hagleyensis'), *H.*'Fairfieldii' × ('Fairfieldensis') and *H.lavaudiana*, as well as other cultivars like *H.*'Colwall', *H.*'Walter Buccleugh' and *H.*'Morning Clouds'. Leaves and young shoots become discoloured and distorted and in severe attacks turn black and die. Remove affected leaves and shoots and spray thoroughly with a copper oxychloride spray or Dithane 945 and repeat at two-weekly intervals until the disease no longer appears. Downy mildew (*Peronospora grisea*) is more troublesome in the autumn and winter, during misty, moist or muggy weather. Occasionally aphis or greenfly (*Myzus ornatus*), red spider (*Tetranychus urticae*) and white fly (*Trialevrodes vaporariorum*) can attack the young plants of Hebe and Parahebe. Older plants can, under protected cover, be attacked on the under sides of the leaves with scale (*Coccus hesperidum*) against which use a systemic insecticide. Use the appropriate pesticide recommended.

A physiological problem that sometimes arises with the larger leaved Hebes is where the flowering shoot becomes condensed and all floral parts become leaf like. It was thought to be a virus problem, but now it is known that if a shoot has gone into the floral phase of growth and poor conditions occur, namely low light, night temperatures 42°F (5.6°C) and just below and short days, then this trouble can occur. Therefore it is recommended that when taking cuttings in September or October, always take them from growing shoots and *not* from shoots that are flowering or have flower buds beginning to appear.

5
Propagation of Hebes and Parahebes

Sooner or later gardeners have that inbred desire to raise their own plants. Propagation is a fascinating art, which all can practise and for which 'green fingers' are not essential. A little knowledge, of where the plant grows in the wild and the climate it grows in, is not a dangerous thing as it can make the success of raising new plants more likely. Shrubs and subshrubs can be propagated in two ways, either by seed or vegetative means, where certain parts of the plant, such as leaves, stems or roots, are used to produce that new plant. In the wild, Hebes propagate themselves mainly by seed: this can be a slower process to produce a mature bush than by vegetative means. Plants from seed can show slight variations in height, habit and flowering ability, whereas plants propagated by vegetative means reproduce exactly the characteristics of the parent plant.

Hebes from Seed

Hebe species, say *Hebe odora*, will come true from seed, if pollinated by the same species, in this case *Hebe odora*. If, however, a species is pollinated by an entirely different species, then you will get a hybrid, which may or may not bear a resemblance to either of the parents. Only crosses between two species can produce hybrids, whereas a species crossed with a cultivated variety will produce a variant, or another cultivar as it is now called. Two cultivars crossed will also produce another cultivar or variant even if they are the same and not different cultivars. One fact that is constant is that when Hebes cross or hybridise, neither parent is dominant, so the resulting progeny is always half-way between one parent and the other in leaf length, shape and colour, also colour of stems, leaves and flowers, as well as eventual height.

Some Hebes, especially the larger leaved cultivars, will produce viable seed as evidenced by the seedlings that appear around the bushes. A *Hebe speciosa* cultivar produces many seeds; these seeds are fairly light in weight and there could be as many as 30,000 seeds to the ounce (1,060 seeds to the gram). As Hebes cross readily, more often than not the seedlings that arise do not vary very much from the parent around which they are found, so it is better to destroy them, than be tempted to plant them elsewhere in the garden. Only rarely do you find the seedling that is different, if you do, then you can grow it on, assessing its growth, colour of leaves and stems and the colour and shape of its flowers. Even then, you may find it is no better than existing cultivars, so it is better to scrap it, however hard the decision. The present confusion within Hebe, where some cultivars have more than one name and some have even five names, has been caused by gardeners giving the chance seedling or cultivar a name, before checking whether there is the same cultivar or a cultivar very similar to it already in cultivation. *Hebe* 'Youngii' was sent unnamed to this country by a nurseryman in Otago, New Zealand and when it was sold to British gardeners it had been renamed *Hebe* 'Carl Teschner' after the nurseryman who had sent it.

Before naming or renaming a Hebe, there is a recognised procedure to follow and this is gone into in detail in Chapter 6.

Sowing Hebe Seed

For sowing seed of a Hebe species, one should use either a John Innes type seed compost or a moss peat and sand plant raising compost. The seed can be sown in a small pan or seed tray. Evenly press down the compost to leave a fairly firm, level surface. Next water well with a fine rosed can. After draining, re-level the surface with some sharp sand or grit and sow the fairly small seed thinly over the surface. Cover the seed with the same sharp sand or grit and lightly firm. Put the pan or tray on the propagation bench or into a propagator and cover with a sheet of glass or clear plastic film. The bench should be in good light and out of direct sun. Provide a germinating temperature of 54–60°F (12–15°C). Turn the glass over daily to remove condensation; water only when needed. Be patient as the seed may take a little while to germinate, especially the smaller leaved and mountain species, which can take several months. With mountain species putting the seed in the refrigerator (not the freezer) for 2–3 weeks might assist the germination.

Filling pan with compost

Evenly firming compost to leave surface level

Sowing seed thinly and spaced uniformly

5.1 Sowing Hebe seed

Vegetative Propagation of Hebes and Parahebes

The vegetative propagation of Hebes is mainly by cuttings grown in cool conditions, at temperatures of 54–60°F (12–15°C), as for seed germination. Too high a temperature can result in a loss of cuttings by rotting or drying out. As a routine precaution, spray over the cuttings with a fungicide such as Thiram or Benlate to prevent rotting, especially if covering with plastic.

Taking cuttings from the right material, in the right condition, increases the certainty of successful rooting. Do not take shoots for cuttings from:

Old wood or aged bushes or plants.
Bushes desiccated by wind or drought.
Bushes damaged by frost, weedkiller, etc.
Diseased, pest damaged or weak bushes.
Bushes where the naming is in doubt.
Bushes where the flowering is poor or late or the growth not typical.

With the whipcord Hebes, young shoots will often not form roots and more mature wood or one year old wood can give better results. With the larger leaved Hebes and the taller growing, narrow leaved Hebes, stem

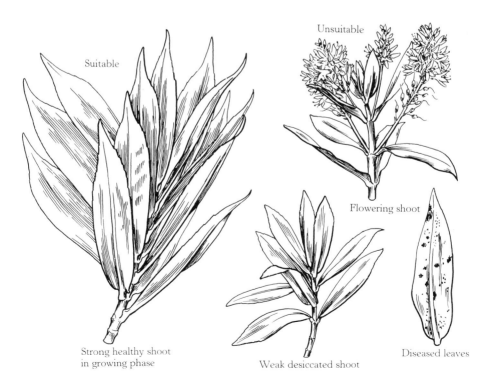

5.2 Suitable and unsuitable shoots for cuttings

cuttings should always be taken from the growth shoots as the flowers are usually terminal, ie at the ends of the stems. It can happen that a cutting from a flower shoot will root and not grow, because the growth buds, which are lower down the stem, have been cut off in making the cutting.

Propagation of young, strong, healthy growth shoots can be carried out from when the shoots are long enough and up to mid September. It is possible to take cuttings, from plants, overwintered under glass or shelter, from late January to extend the propagation period. For successful rooting, it is better if the growing young shoots are not too soft and liable to easy wilting. When collecting cuttings, put the shoots into a polythene bag straightaway and keep the bag in a cool place and out of the sun until they are prepared and inserted.

Preparation and Insertion of Cuttings

Type	Length of cutting		Approx. pairs of leaves		Time till first roots
	(in)	(cm)	Left on	Removed	(in days)
(a) *Hebes*					
Long or large leaved	3–3½	8–9	3–4	2–3	21–28
Medium leaved					
¾–1½ in (1.9–3.8 cm)	3	8	5–7	3–4	21–56
Small leaved					
¼–½ in (0.6–1.3 cm)	2–2½	5–7	7–10	7–9	35–70
Very small leaved	2	5	10–14	7–9	42–84
(b) *Parahebes*					
Larger leaved	2½	6–7	9–10	5	21–28
Smaller leaved	2½	6–7	9–12	3–5	35–70

After preparing the cuttings they are inserted in pans or trays; or individually in small pots 2¾ × 2¾ in (7 × 7 cm) square in the case of the large and long, narrow leaved Hebes. The advantage of the individual pots, which fit 15 to a standard seed tray, is there is no disturbance of the roots when potted on. Even the stronger growing medium leaved Hebes respond well to this method of growing.

Before inserting, the cuttings can have their ends dipped in a hormone rooting powder, as instructed on the container. There are different types of rooting powder for softwood cuttings and for semi-mature and whipcord cuttings.

The pans, pots and trays are filled with either a John Innes soil or a peat and sand soilless compost. (John Innes Formula – 2 parts sterilised loam, 1 part sphagnum moss peat, 1 part coarse sand plus up to 4 oz (113 g) ground limestone or chalk and 2 oz (56.5 g) base fertiliser per bushel (36 litres). Soilless compost formula – equal parts sphagnum moss peat and coarse sand or grit, plus the same amount of ground limestone or chalk, and base fertiliser, as for John Innes Formula.) A dibber is used to make the holes in the compost for the cuttings, as cuttings can be bruised by

32

Cut cleanly below leaf joint
or node

5.3 Preparing and inserting Hebe cuttings

pushing them into the compost. With the smaller leaved Hebe and Parahebe cuttings, such as *H*.'Carnosula' and *H*.'Pagei', which take longer to
root, it is worth trying composts made up of half sphagnum moss peat
(medium grade) and half grit or sharp sand.

An alternative to sharp sand or grit is medium grade vermiculite; this is
light in weight, warm feeling and holds many times its own weight in
water. It is made from sterile, laminated mica mineral subjected to high
temperature, which expands it into concertina like granules with very
many open cells. Attention was drawn to this material when sending
rooted cuttings to New Zealand, as it is the only material that the New
Zealand Ministry of Agriculture and Fisheries will allow on the roots; all
other materials have to be thoroughly washed off before sending the
cuttings. This prompted the use of vermiculite in rooting Hebe cuttings.
Vermiculite on its own means constant attention to watering as the
material is free draining and so can dry out. Adding medium grade sphagnum moss peat helped retain the moisture and slowed down the drying
out. With a vermiculite compost it was found that cuttings made roots
throughout the compost in the pot and there was almost 100 per cent
rooting, especially with the medium and large leaved Hebes.

For a vermiculite cuttings compost, use equal parts of medium grade
vermiculite (granule size .08–0.2 in, 2–5 mm) and medium grade sphagnum moss peat. Mix thoroughly together and repeat occasionally whilst
filling pots or pans as the vermiculite, if dry, tends to settle to the bottom
of the container. With vermiculite compost, it is an advantage to use individual pots for the medium and larger leaved Hebe cuttings. The cutting
forms roots right through the compost and, with no disturbance when
potting on, it can mean a larger plant sooner with a good root system at
planting time.

After inserting the cuttings give a thorough watering in and, as an insurance, spray the cuttings with a fungicide like Maneb (Dithane 945) to prevent downy mildew, or Thiram for leaf spots, etc. With vermiculite compost it may be necessary to give one or two further thorough waterings to make sure the granules have taken up the full amount of water. Trays or pans of cuttings can be made to feel at home or mist benches, plastic covered frames, or even covered with a sheet of thin clear plastic put on top of the cuttings. Propagators or glass covered frames can be used or a shaded cold frame in summertime.

Parahebe perfoliata (Digger's Speedwell) has underground stems. To obtain another plant or plants, pot into small pots short to medium length shoots with a piece of underground stem attached.

Pot on all cuttings as soon as they are well rooted and grow on, in cool, airy conditions and not allowing them to dry out at the roots. Overhead damping after sunny days is helpful to Hebes and keeps away red spider in glasshouses and structures.

Layering

Some carpeting Hebes, like *H.*'Youngii' (*H.*'Carl Teschner'), *H.*'County Park' and *H.*'Wingletye', and Parahebes like *P.catarractae* or *P.lyallii* will layer naturally or can be induced to layer into the soil by pegging down. Some compost worked into the soil will help the rooting. It is known that *Hebe* × 'Franciscana' can also be layered, by pegging down some of the lower branches, just as a shrub is layered. It could be that there are other Hebes that will respond to this method of propagation.

When the layer is found to be well rooted, remove from parent plant by a clean cut just behind the roots. By potting up the rooted layer, one can make more sure of successfully raising a new plant.

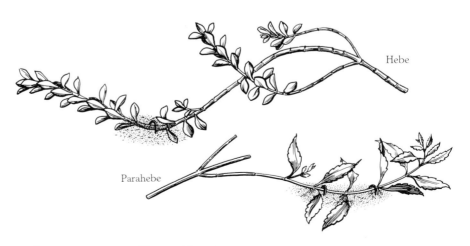

5.4 Layering ground cover Hebes and Parahebes

6
The naming of Hebes

For the uninitiated it might be helpful to say first of all how plants are named. Plants are classified by botanists according to their flower types and those with a similar flower type are grouped first of all into a FAMILY. The family Scrophulariaceae has about 250 genera of small trees, shrubs, annual and perennial plants, including HEBE. Hebe is separated from the other members of the family in having funnel shaped flowers split into four equal lobes at the end and, if there is a fifth, it is smaller. As has been mentioned earlier, the seed capsule splits horizontally. Each member of the family is called botanically a GENUS and within the genus HEBE have been gathered about 100 SPECIES having common characters, but varying in foliage, size or colour, habit of growth, etc.

In 1952, an International Botanical Conference was held and drew up the Horticultural Code of Nomenclature which laid down the rules governing the naming of plants from then on. Plants had had Latinised names and the term VARIETY referred to both a natural and a man made variant of a species; but from 1952, VARIETY refers to a slightly differing group, within a species, found in the wild only — for example, *Hebe stricta* var. *macroura*. Where man takes a hand, this plant is now called a CULTIVAR (cultivated variety shortened to 'cultivar'). Even where the plant produces or sports a shoot with variegated foliage and this has to be propagated vegetatively, this is still a CULTIVAR. *Hebe* 'Midsummer Beauty', itself a cultivar, branch sported the cream, green and plum leaved cultivar *Hebe* 'Lopen'.

In 1955, the International Registration Authorities for various genera of plants were established. The International Registration Authority for HEBE is the Royal New Zealand Institute of Horticulture. The Registrar is Mr L.J. Metcalf, Director of Parks and Recreation Department, Invercargill, New Zealand, who has just completed the preparation of the International Check List of Names of Hebe Cultivars.

What are the procedures that should be followed, if you have raised a cultivar, worthy of growing, sufficiently distinct from other known varieties and cultivars and is as far as you can see, strong, healthy and free from proneness to pest and disease attack? To start with, it will need a name and that name will have to be acceptable to the Controller of Plant Variety Rights and conform to the procedures laid down, which are:

(1) Latinised names must be avoided, e.g. *Hebe* 'Smithii'. The name

should be markedly different from the Latin and in common language, e.g. *Hebe* 'Emerald Green' or *Hebe* 'Autumn Glory'.

(2) Numerals and symbols should not be used, for example *Hebe* 'Smith's No. 1'.

(3) There should be no initial article. *Hebe* 'The Favourite' would have to be *Hebe* 'Favourite', except where linguistic custom demands, e.g. 'La Favourite'.

(4) The name should consist of one or two words and not more than three. The word 'variety' or 'form' should not be in the name, e.g. *Hebe* 'Smith's Variety'.

(5) The cultivar must not be given the name of another plant, for example, *Hebe* 'Heather', but where it is part of a lady's name it could be accepted like *Hebe* 'Heather Smith'.

(6) Names should not have abbreviations or forms of address; the exception is 'Mrs'. *Hebe* 'Mrs Smith', although correct, would be better identified if it contained initials such as Mrs C.P. Smith. *Hebe* 'C.P. Smith' would not be acceptable but, if the husband, then it should be *Hebe* 'Charles P. Smith'. If Mr Smith was knighted then it would be *Hebe* 'Sir Charles Smith'. It is national custom to include the 'Sir'. Miss or Ms Smith would also not be acceptable, it would have to be *Hebe* 'Mary Smith'.

(7) The name suggested should not confuse with any existing name of a variety or cultivar. *Hebe* 'Frimley Gem' would certainly confuse with *Hebe* 'Primley Gem'.

(8) Long names, unpronounceable names and superlatives are frowned on; also vague epithets which could equally apply to other similar cultivars. So, if you had thought of naming your Hebe after that village in Anglesey with the long and unpronounceable name, then forget it!

Having decided on a name, then you will need to register this cultivar. This work is being undertaken by the Hebe Society in collaboration with the Registration Authority in New Zealand. Details of the Hebe Society are to be found in Appendix 3. The Registrar appointed by the Hebe Society will check your suggested name against the International Check List and will say if it is acceptable, as well as sending you a registration form on which to record full details of flower, foliage, height and habit, with suggestions as to possible parentage. By the time this book is in print the Hebe Society hopes to have set up a National Reference Collection of Hebes and Parahebes in West Cornwall.

The procedure and rules for naming refer to all genera and are recognised and observed internationally. There has been much confusion with the naming of Hebe cultivars and varieties, but efforts have been made to overcome this confusion in the last ten years culminating in the preparing for printing of an International Check List of Hebes. With the setting up of a registration service and a National Reference Collection by the Hebe

Society, confusion could be a thing of the past, especially if everyone follows the 1952 plant naming code.

For those considering naming Hebes, it is commended that they read the fascinating story in Appendix 1 of *Hebe* × 'Franciscana', which brings to light the unrewarding work involved in unravelling the confusion surrounding this cultivar.

7

Choosing Hebes and Parahebes

There are a variety of uses to which Hebes and Parahebes can be put in the garden. Whether the garden is large or small Hebes fit in well with other plants, be it in the shrub border, the rock garden or the conifer bed.

In the shrub border they provide flower and foliage colour, shape and texture, either as background or subjects in their own right. The whipcord Hebes are at home either in the shrub border or in the conifer bed or used instead of conifers. Bronze foliaged Hebes come into their own in winter as the colour deepens in leaves and stems and this gives an added interest to the shrub border.

Hebes can provide ground covering and carpeting, both for the small garden or larger park. *Hebe pinguifolia* 'Sutherlandii', for example, has been found to be a very suitable shrub for the larger areas. For the smaller garden *Hebe* 'Youngii' is very popular as a ground covering plant.

Informal hedges, or low hedges to line paths, can be provided by the Hebe. Rock gardens, small, medium sized or large, provide ideal sites for the hummock forming, lower growing and spreading Hebes and Parahebes. Even the trough can be the home for the smaller cushion forming or carpeting Hebes.

Many are attracted by the more colourful, less hardy Hebes. These, too, can be planted and grown outside in summer in tubs or large pots or bedded out in early summer to augment the floral display. Containers will be brought in during September to overwinter in a frost free greenhouse or conservatory. Cuttings are taken in August from the bedded out Hebes to root and grow, frost free overwinter, to be bedded out in the following year.

There are Hebes for all these purposes and the task is to find those that are most suitable. To help in the search here are some suggestions.

Troughs or Small Rock Gardens

The requirements are for plants that are not too large or vigorous, plants that will form neat hummocks or cushions and less vigorous and neater carpeting or spreading plants to cover rocks or spread over the side of the trough. Also upright growing, small shrubs to give height and catch the eye with flower or foliage. There is a need for the plants to be evergreen and long flowering.

Hummocks or Cushions — *H.buchananii*, *H.colensoi* var. *glauca*, *H.*'Emerald Green'.

Carpeting or Spreading — *H.canterburiensis*, *H.*'Pagei', *H.pimeleoides* 'Quick Silver', *H.*'Prostrata', *H.*'Wingletye', *H.*'Youngii', *Parahebe decora* ('Bidwillii') 'Kea' or 'Rose Hybrid', *P.* 'Gillian', *P.lyallii*.

Upright Growing and Rounded — *H.*'Colwall', *H.*'Edinensis', *H.laingii*, *H.*'Loganioides', *H.pinguifolia*, *H.*'Polly Moore', *H.raoulii* var. *pentasepala*.

Larger Rock Gardens and Small Borders

With the rock garden the requirements are the same as for smaller rock gardens, only larger plants are needed for the pockets between the rocks and spreading over the rocks.

More upright plants are needed for the border, with lower growing and spreading plants for the front of the border. Here are the suggestions for possible hardy hebes to use:

'Pocket' Fillers — *H.*'Boscawenii', *H.*'Carnosula', *H.*'Pewter Dome', *H.vernicosa*.

Carpeters and Spreaders — *H.*'Bowles' Variety', *H.*'County Park', *H.hectori* var. *demissa*, *H.*'Wingletye', *Parahebe catarractae* and cultivars 'Miss Wilmott' and 'Porlock Purple'.

Upright, Rounded Shrubs — *H.albicans*, *H.*'Bowles' Hybrid', *H.*'Caledonia', *H.cupressoides* 'Boughton Dome', *H.pauciramosa*.

Less Hardy Hebes for Coastal or Milder Areas — *H.*'Fairfieldii', *H.*'Hagley Park', *H.hulkeana*, *H.maerantha*.

Ground Cover

In gardens, parks and other areas, there is always the need for low growing, spreading shrubs to reduce ground maintenance and weeds. *H.pinguifolia* 'Sutherlandii', after its success on traffic islands in New Zealand, is recommended as a ground covering shrub as it grows only to a height of 15 in (37 cm) but has an eventual spread of 36 in (90 cm). This would be too large for the smaller garden, whereas the popular *H.*'Youngii' might be more suitable, growing to a height of 4 in (10 cm) and spreading to 18–24 in (45–60 cm).

Smaller Ground Coverers — *H.*'Buxifolia Nana', *H.chathamica* (coastal gardens), *H.*'County Park', *H.*'Edinensis', *H.*'Youngii' (*H.*'Carl Teschner'), *Parahebe catarractae* and cultivars.

Larger Ground Coverers — *H.pauciramosa*, *H.pinguifolia* 'Sutherlandii', *H.propinqua*, *H.rakaiensis*.

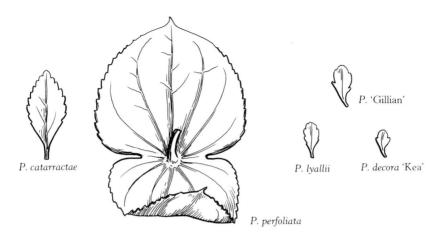

P. 'Gillian'

P. catarractae

P. lyallii   P. decora 'Kea'

P. perfoliata

7.1 Differing leaf shapes of Parahebes

Medium Sized Borders

Hebes not only fit in well with other shrubs but they can, on their own, provide what is required. So in what ways can Hebes help in the border? The foliage and stems provide colour, especially in winter, as well as acting as a foil to other shrubs. The whipcords add texture as well as colour and interest. Hebes with their white flowers provide a foil, as well as preventing colour clashes between the more colourful shrubs in the border. Some Hebes flower in late spring, others flower in August or early September, times of the year where there could be gaps in flowering of the other shrubs in the border.

Hardier Hebes

Foliage and Earlier Flowering — *H.*'Edington', *H.*'Eversley Seedling', *H.glaucophylla* 'Variegata', *H.*'Primley Gem'

Foliage and Later Flowering — *H.*'Autumn Glory', *H.*'Mrs Winder', *H.*'Warleyensis' (*H.*'Warley').

Whipcords — *H.hectori*, *H.ochracea*, *H.ochracea* 'James Stirling'.

White Flowered — *H.odora* 'New Zealand Gold', *H.*'Spender's Seedling'.

Less Hardy Hebes

For Milder and Coastal Areas — *H.*'Dorothy Peach', *H.*× 'Franciscana Variegata', *H.*'Inspiration', *H.*'Lindsayii', *H.*'Sapphire', *H.*'Watson's Pink'.

Background and Screening

A use for the larger, taller growing Hebes may be to provide shelter and a foil or neutral background to the more colourful plants and shrubs planted in front. In coastal districts the problem could be salt laden winds, in which case *H.dieffenbachii*, *H.×* 'Franciscana', and *H.salicifolia* could be used. For screening elsewhere:

H.'Blush Wand', *H.*'C.P. Raffill', *H.*'Midsummer Beauty', *H.*'Miss E. Fittall', *H.*'Violet Wand', *H.*'White Wand'.

Hedges up to 36 in (90 cm)

The need here is for shrubs that are upright growing and not spreading, if possible. The Hebes need to be fairly compact and reasonably fast in growth.

H.'Buxifolia' (British), *H.*'Spender's Seedling', *H.*'Primley Gem', *H.*'Waikiki'.

Low Hedge for Edge of Border — *H.*'Buxifolia Nana', *H.*'Edinensis'.

Hedges over 36 in (90 cm)

The same requirements here as for the lower hedging. Spreading growths can be trimmed back, after frosts have gone in spring, and again in early August.

Coastal — *H.brachysiphon* (slow growing), *H.dieffenbachii*, *H.×* 'Franciscana'.

Inland — *H.*'C.P. Raffill', *H.*'Midsummer Beauty', *H.*'Miss E. Fittall'.

Mild Areas — *H.*'Great Orme', *H.*'Jewel'.

Tubs, Large Pots or Bedding Out

The less hardy, large leaved Hebes, with the showy and richly coloured flowers or foliage, need more sheltered sites where there is little frost or cold piercing wind. These Hebes make ideal shrubs for growing in tubs, large pots or for bedding out. These Hebes grown in pots and tubs are put outside on the patio after frosts have gone and then re-housed in autumn and grown in glass houses, conservatories or room extensions, provided they are frost free overwinter: in the same way as, say, Fuchsias, only they are not dried off but allowed to grow on.

The second way to grow these tender or less hardy Hebes is to treat them like Pelargoniums — taking cuttings in early August, rooting them in shady, cool conditions under glass, where they grow on till frosts are gone, then bedding out with other bedding plants, or on their own. In autumn, good plants can be potted up for overwintering in a frost free glasshouse for planting out the following year.

Less hardy Hebes for these suggested ways of growing are:

Taller Growing — *H.*'Andersonii Anne Pimm', *H.*'Andersonii Aurea', *H.*'Andersonii Variegata', *H.*'Highdownensis', *H.*'La Seduisante', *H.*'Purple Queen', *H.*'Simon Delaux'.

Lower Growing — *H.*'Headfortii', *H.*'Inspiration', *H.*'Purple Tips', *H.*'Rubella', *H.*'Sapphire', *H.*'Watson's Pink'.

There are some hardy Hebes that might be considered if this style of growing meets a need:

H.'Amanda Cook', *H.*'Edington', *H.glaucophylla* 'Variegata', *H.gracillima*, *H.odora* 'New Zealand Gold', *H.*'Spender's Seedling'.

8
Hebe species, varieties and cultivars

For the botanists and horticulturists, the Hebe species have been well documented in the *Flora of New Zealand*, Volume 1 compiled by the late Dr H.H. Allan and his assistant Dr L. Moore. Dr Allan was Head of the Botany Division of the Department of Scientific and Industrial Research at Lincoln, near Christchurch, South Island NZ where there is an extensive herbarium of native New Zealand plans including Hebe and Parahebe.

Until the updated Hebe International Check List of Cultivars is available, there is no accurate figure as to the number of cultivars there are. Several cultivars have acquired other names over the years, for example *H.*'Youngii' is known as *H.*'Carl Teschner' in Britain. Where these synonymous names are known they have been included in the descriptions. No doubt further synonyms will be appearing in the International Check List. With a number of Hebes it still has to be decided whether they are or are not true species and in a very few cases whether they are Parahebes or Hebes. Just recently, *Hebe* 'Gutheriana', also known as *H.*'Brill Blue', was removed from *Hebe* as it is really a Veronica although it is evergreen. In future, this prostrate plant, with very small, dark green leaves and bright blue flowers in summer will be known as *Veronica* 'Gutheriana'.

With the Hebe Society setting up a National Reference Collection and offering a registration service for new cultivars, the confusion with synonymous names will be gradually overcome, but it will need every raiser's co-operation to prevent confusion in the future.

In New Zealand there are more species than cultivars. The Otari Native Plant Museum in Wellington, North Island, has a good collection of Hebe species. On the South Island in Hagley Park, Christchurch, the Cockayne Memorial Garden, in memory of Dr L. Cockayne, has Hebes interestingly displayed in island beds and borders. in Appendix 3 are other Botanic Gardens and Parks where one can see Hebes and Parahebes.

In Britain the reverse is the case; there are many more cultivars than species. Some of the gardens where collections of Hebes can be seen are given in Appendix 3; this list is far from complete and it is hoped that the Hebe Society will compile a more comprehensive list.

The Hardy Plant Society has recently issued *The Plant Finder*, listing 22,000 plants including over 275 Hebes, 30 Parahebes and other New Zealand plants like Metrosideros, Phormium, and even Chionohebe. Where these can be bought or found is also given. No doubt this will find its way to gardening clubs and libraries as well as to plant-seeking garden-

Most Hebes, whether large or small, are to some extent rounded in outline, except those that are prostrate or the whipcords which are spiky in appearance. A species example of each type of habit is given.

Prostrate, carpeting or ground hugging
— *H.*'Youngii' (*H.*'Carl Teschner')

Spreading, — wider than tall
— *H.rakaiensis*

Dome shaped
— *H.* 'Pewter Dome'

Rounded (small)
— *H.vernicosa*

Loose or open growth
— *H.*'carnosula'

Compact or neat habit
— *H.*'Watson's Pink'

Semi erect habit
— *H.*'Spender's Seedling'

Erect habit of growth
— *H.*'Buxifolia' (Britain)

Whipcord, leaves wrap around
the stems — *H.ochracea*

8.1 *Hebe habits of growth, illustrating terms used in alphabetical list*

ers. To obtain a copy apply to The Hardy Plant Society, Freepost, Worcester WR2 4BR.

Explanatory Notes

The descriptions follow a more or less set pattern: origin, with meaning of the name; habit of the plant; the leaves including shape, colour and other features; the flowers including colour and how they are carried, either in spikes or racemes, as well as time of flowering; and finally hardiness and the possible uses in the garden.

The Hebe species are written like this — *H.albicans*, whereas the cultivars are written this way — *H.*'Amanda Cook'. Should it be a natural variety then it is written — *H.pimeleoides* var. *rupestris*. Where (IS) appears after the name, it means that the botanists have yet to make up their minds as to whether it is a true species or its origin is not known. IS is Latin for 'incertae sedis' and means a plant of uncertain origin, for example — *H.*'Carnosula' (IS).

Measurements for heights, length of leaf blade etc. are given in imperial as well as metric measure.

Habits of growth, like prostrate, spreading, rounded and so on, are illustrated in Figure 8.1. Botanical terms used are explained, unless in common usage.

Eventual heights given are average, because plant growth can vary with climate, exposure or shelter, height above sea level and soil conditions.

Hardiness can vary with surroundings. Hebes growing amongst other shrubs often survive lower temperatures than they would if planted on their own. See p. 00 for the hardiness zone maps and hardiness zone chart. For convenience, the zone figures for Great Britain are repeated below:

	Fahrenheit	Celsius
Zone 7	0 to 10	−17 to −12
Zone 8	10 to 20	−12 to − 7
Zone 9	20 to 30	− 7 to − 1
Zone 10	30 to 40	− 1 to 5

WARNING   With some of the less hardy Hebes, the Zone Hardiness figure has been given as 9(10). This means that this species or cultivar will only survive outdoors in sites protected from chilling winds or away from frost pockets. It is wise to provide some cover if possible when very low temperatures are forecast. Growing one or two replacement plants under cover during winter is an insurance against the occasional severe winter that might badly damage or kill your Hebe.

Hebe Species, Varieties and Cultivars

H.acutiflora

(Latin — acutus = sharp, flora = flower) Found under the falls of Keri-keri, North Island, NZ, and first collected there by A. Cunningham in 1838.

A small, erect shrub, with few branches and spreading leaves; the branchlets are glabrous to lightly downy. Grows to a height of up to 12 in (30 cm). The leaves are linear lanceolate with minute, marginal hairs; length 1¾–3 in (4.5–7.5 cm); width c. ¼ in (5–7 mm). The narrow, pointed, white or faintly lavender flowers are carried towards the ends of the branchlets, in early summer.

Zone 10; tender.

H.'Adamsii'

Named after one of the finders (T.F. Cheeseman and J. Adams). Originated from the North Cape District, North Island, NZ in 1896. A possible hybrid between *H.ligustrifolia* and *H.macrocarpa* var. *brevifolia*.

A stout branched, rounded, medium to large bush, growing up to 3 ft 6 in (107 cm). the linear lanceolate, mid-green leaves have a leathery appearance; length 2½ in (6.5 cm); width ½ in (1.25 cm). The flowers are rather crowded near the ends of the branches, purple in colour and fairly large in size, in summer.

Zone 10; tender.

H. × 'Affinis'

(Latin — affinis = related) T.F. Cheeseman gave this name, as the plant he had found was intermediate between the two parents *H.macrocarpa* and *H.stricta* or variety of it. A natural hybrid, it grows on the cliffs and coasts in the Waitamata and Manukau districts, North Island, NZ-

An erect to spreading shrub, with yellow green, slightly hairy stems. In New Zealand gardens it grows up to 6 ft (180 cm) in height. The leaves are light green, lanceolate to oblong lanceolate, dull gloss above, paler beneath; length 2½–3¼ in (6.5–8 cm); width ½–¾ in (1.25–2 cm). The leaf bud is without a sinus. The flowers are carried in spikes up to 7 in (18 cm), white in colour, appearing in early spring. The drooping spikes give this shrub a graceful appearance.

Tender. An attractive shrub for coastal districts. A garden shrub in New Zealand, worth trying in Britain. Zone 10.

H.albicans

(Latin — albicans = white or whitish) Originated in the mountains of Nelson Province, where it is found in rocky places and subalpine scrub between 3,500 and 4,500 ft (1,066–1,371 m). A South Island species.

A low growing, spreading and much branched shrub. The branchlets are stout, with fairly long hairs, green at first, ageing dark brown. Grows

48

up to 2 ft (60 cm) in Britain; up to 4 ft (120 cm) in New Zealand. The leaves are ovate, glaucous on upper and lower surfaces, so giving the grey green appearance of the foliage; length up to 1¼ in (3 cm); width ½ in (1.25 cm). The white flowers are densely packed in short spikes up to ¾ in (2 cm) in length, at the ends of the branchlets, in summer.

Hardy anywhere in Britain. A worthwhile garden plant, neat, striking appearance and wealth of flower in summer. Zone 8 or could be lower.

H.albicans 'Prostrate Form'

A low growing, up to 12 in (30 cm), spreading form of H.albicans with same grey green, glaucous foliage. Also known as H.(albicans)'Sussex Carpet'. A front of border, rock garden or ground cover plant, with short spikes of white flowers in July. Hardy. Zone. 8, like parent.

H.'Alicia Amherst'

Named after Alicia Amherst (1865–1941), writer and horticulturist. H.'Veitchii' and H.'Royal Purple' are now said to be synonymous. H.'Veitchii' was raised by Messrs Veitch in Exeter in 1911, and there could be slight differences as with a similar hybrid raised in New Zealand; but overall they are too alike to separate. H.speciosa is in its parentage.

A strong growing, much branched and erect shrub, branchlets reddish at first, ageing green or brownish green, growing to a height of 4 ft (120 cm) or more. The leaves are elliptic to broadly elliptic, narrowing at the base, dark green in colour, shiny but paler below; length 4–4½ in (10–11.5 cm); width 1¾–2 in (4.5–5 cm). The leaves are upward at first then spreading. The flowers are royal purple in colour, in spikes up to 6 in (15 cm) in length and 1–1½ in (2.5–4 cm) in diameter, in late summer.

A fine shrub for the sheltered, almost frost free border. Zone 9 (10).

H.'Amanda Cook'

A branch sport on H.'Autumn Glory' found and grown on by Brian Cook in Warwickshire and to which he has given his daughter's name. Raised in 1980. The leaves vary from the parent in having variable yellow margining, otherwise it is the same in size and shape.

See H.'Autumn Glory' for full details of habit, flower, etc.

H.'Amethyst'

A seedling from a cross between H.'Great Orme' and H.'Waikiki' that arose at Polden Acres Garden, Somerset in 1979.

Erect growing, with brown stems and spreading leaves, to about 30 in (76 cm) in height. The leaves are oval oblong, mid green in colour but paler below; length 1¾–2 in (4.5–5 cm); width ⁴⁄₁₀ in (1 cm). The leaves have a tendency to turn in one plane. Pale amethyst flowers are carried in 1½–2 in (3.75–5 cm) spikes, during summer and autumn, towards the ends of the stems.

A border shrub. Zone 10, or even Zone 9 in sheltered sites.

H.amplexicaulis

(Latin — amplexicaulis = clasping; refers to the leaf base clasping the stem) Originated in tussock grassland of the Rangitata and Mt. Peel mountains of Canterbury, South Island, NZ and was found by J.F. Armstrong in 1869.

A small decumbent shrub, 10–20 in (25–50 cm) in height, growing over the rocks amongst the tussock grass. The stems are stout and glabrous (hairless) with tips growing upward. The leaves are broadly oblong, slightly concave, thick and leathery. There is a tendency for the leaves to overlap; length ½–⅗ in (1.2–1.5 cm); width ¼–½ in (0.6–1.25 cm). Short, compact spikes, of white flowers, length ⅗ in (1.5 cm), are carried at the ends of the stems in midsummer. The spikes are usually in pairs.

Hardy rock plant. Zone 8, or could be lower.

H.amplexicaulis forma *hirta*

(Latin — hirta = hairy or shaggy, which distinguishes this form). Previously *H.allanii* in the *Flora of New Zealand* (Dr H.H. Allan) and changed in 1987. Found in rocky outcrops in tussock grassland on Mt. Peel, Canterbury, South Island, NZ, from 1,300–4,000 ft (305–1,220 m).

A low growing, spreading shrub up to 12 in (30 cm) in height, with stout branchlets covered in woolly hair. The oblong, thick rather leathery, grey green leaves are covered with rather long white hairs or woolly pubescence, often short or absent along the reddish margins, which makes this form distinctive; length ¾ in (2 cm); width ¼ in (0.6 cm). Short spikes of white flowers ¾ in (0.8 cm) in length, hairy and rather erect, appear in summer.

A very good shrub for the rock garden in New Zealand and possibly in Britain. Zone 7; very hardy.

H.'Amy'

Raised at St Anne's Gardens, Dublin, Eire and named after Lady Amy Ardilaun. It was introduced by Treseders of Truro, Cornwall.

Erect growing, yet rounded in outline; the branchlets are deep bronze in colour supporting the spreading leaves; height 54 in (137 cm). The leaves are obovate elliptic, intense dark bronze in colour; length up to 1½ in (4 cm); width ½–⅗ in (1.25–1.50 cm). The under surfaces of the upper leaves are also deep bronze. Short spikes, 1½ in (4 cm) long, carry bright violet flowers, in summer.

A showy cultivar for the sheltered gardens, mainly frost free or near the coast. Zone 10, not hardy.

H.'Andersonii'

Named by Isaac Anderson-Henry (1800–1884) of Maryfield near Edinburgh, who raised this Hebe by crossing *H.speciosa* (male) with *H.salicifolia* (female), prior to 1849.

A strong growing, large leaved shrub, rounded in outline; height up to

5 feet (152 cm), spread can be up to 4 ft (120 cm). The leaves are ovate lanceolate, mid to dark green, lighter below; length 4 in (10 cm); width 1 in (2.5 cm). The vein pattern is noticeable on the upward turned leaves. Closely placed, light violet flowers are carried on long 4 in (10 cm) spikes, in summer.

A cultivar for the protected frost free garden. Zone 10.

H.'Andersonii Anne Pimm'

How and where this cultivar originated is not known.

A neat rounded shrub, not as vigorous as H.'Andersonii', growing to a height of 48 in (120 cm). The leaves are ovate, mid-green with slight grey down, which will rub off, margins cream, varying in depth around the leaf. The veining on the upper surface is deeper green and on the lower surface the veins are prominent and the colour lighter; length 2–2½ in (5–6.5 cm); width ¾–1¼ in (1.8–3 cm). Medium length spikes, 2½–3 in (6.5–7.5 cm), carry the pinky purple flowers, in summer.

A less hardy cultivar for the sheltered or coastal garden. Useful for tubs as it grows more slowly and up to about 4 ft (120 cm). Zone 10.

H.'Andersonii Aurea'

A cultivar similar in growth, height, habit, leaf size, flower colour and half hardiness to H.'Andersonii'. The margins of the leaves are yellow of varying width. This variegated cultivar was used for display in conservatories and in summer bedding because of its lack of hardiness.

H.'Andersonii Variegata'

Another variegated shrub similar in growth, leaf size and shape, habit and flower colour to the parent H.'Andersonii'. Again half hardy and was used for display, in a similar way to H.'Andersonii Aurea'. The leaves are irregularly cream banded around the margins.

H.annulata

(Latin — annulus = a ring, hence annulate, ringed or appears to be ringed; refers to the small leaves that ring or sheath the stem). Found among rocks at 2,900 ft (900 m) on northern face of Takitimu Mts, South Island, NZ.

A rather open straggling shrub of the whipcord group, growing to a height of 4–6 in (10–15 cm), with yellow green stems, not glossy, decumbent and straggling. The leaves are very small, ¹/₂₀ in (1 mm) in length, sheathing the stem for ⅓–½ their length, with the tip slightly rounded, yellow green in colour and dull. In short spikes of ten or less, white flowers appear close to the ends of the branchlets, in early summer.

Zone 7; quite hardy.

H.'Anomala'

(Greek — a = not, omalos = equal; Refers to the calyx lobes being either three or four). This plant was discovered by J.F. Armstrong in the head waters of the Rakaia, South Island, NZ. Dr Lucy Moore of NZ considers this to be cultivar of *H.odora.*

Erect growing and much branched, with glossy dark green leaves and, when young, purplish tips to the yellow green branchlets, making this shrub distinctive. In gardens, it grows to 2 ft (60 cm) but can grow up to 3 or 4 ft (90–120 cm). The leaves are linear oblong to elliptic lanceolate, green and shiny above, but paler beneath; length ⅓–¾ in (1–2 cm); width ⅛–⅕ in (3–5 mm). The dark green leaves are also coriaceous or leathery and the leaf bud has a sinus. The flowers are terminal and crowded, forming a short broad panicle of white flowers, in summer. The anthers are purple.

Very hardy, floriferous shrub, better planted in the open and full sun for best effect. An ideal shrub for the border. Zone 7 or less.

H.armstrongii

Discovered at the head of the Rangitata River in 1869 by W. Grey and J.F. Armstrong and named *H.armstrongii* by his brother, J.B. Armstrong. One of the best shrubs of the whipcord group.

A rounded shrub with stout, erect branches, with rather rough, noticeable leaf scars. A little spreading. The branchlets are yellow green to golden and rather crowded, with a tendency to fan out at the ends of the branches. Can grow up to 3 ft (90 cm). The very small leaves, greeny yellow and tightly adpressed to the stems, are joined at their bases for over half the length, which is ⅒ in (2 mm). The leaves are thickened and rounded at the tip. Terminal spikes of white flowers, up to six in number, appear in May and June, but are rather shy to flower in gardens.

A useful conifer like shrub providing a contrasting colour to the green leaved shrubs, so standing out in winter. Zone 7; quite hardy.

H.'Autumn Beauty'

A seedling from *H.'Jewel'* and introduced by the nursery firm, Messrs. Scotts of Merriot, Somerset.

A nicely rounded shrub for the back of the border, with brown stems, with darker brown rings, where the leaves join; fairly well branched. Can grow up to 5 ft (150 cm). The leaves are shiny green, ovate and upward growing; length 1¾–2 in (4–5 cm); width ½ in (1.25 cm). Bright, bluey mauve flowers are carried in spikes, about the length of the leaves and ¾ in (2 cm) or so wide, from late summer and into the autumn.

Zone 10, or a little lower in sheltered borders.

H.'Autumn Blue'

Possibly a hybrid of *H.salicifolia* but other parent not known.

A tall, fairly erect shrub, growing to a height of 60 in (150 cm), with noticeable long, pointed leaves and flower spikes that down curve. The stems are greeny brown in colour with dark brown nodes. The leaves are narrow elliptic, narrowing at the tip to form a point, mid green in colour, paler below, with the vein pattern in evidence; length 4–4¼ in (10–10.5 cm); width ⅘ in (2 cm). Long spikes, of mauvy blue flowers, about the length of the leaves, appear in late summer.

Not for the exposed site although a very good back of the border shrub. Zone 10.

H.'Autumn Glory'

In New Zealand erroneously called 'Autumn Beauty' and 'Autumn Gem'. Dating from around 1900, this originated as a seedling found at White Abbey, Tobarcorran, near Belfast, the garden of General Bland. It was grown on at Smith's, Daisy Hill Nursery at Newry, Co. Down, N. Ireland. *H.pimeleoides* was one parent and *H.* × 'franciscana Blue Gem' is probably the other. As uncertainty exists over the parentage, the suggested cross needs to be made to see if *H.* × 'Franciscana Blue Gem' and *H.pimeleoides* are the parents.

An erect, sparsely branched shrub, which tends to spread, the stems are reddish brown in colour and so, too, are the leaves enclosing the growing buds. Grows up to 30 in (75 cm) in height. The leaves are dark green, paler beneath, often with a reddish margin; length ¾–1 in (2–2½ cm); width ½ in (1.25 cm). The leaf blade is obovate, but elliptic ovate leaves can also be found, as is so with all hybrids from *H.speciosa*, such as *H.* × 'Franciscana Blue Gem'. Short spikes of violet flowers, up to 1¾ in

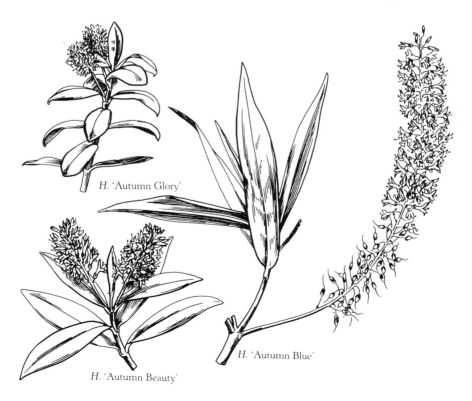

H. 'Autumn Glory'

H. 'Autumn Blue'

H. 'Autumn Beauty'

8.2 'The Autumns': H.'Autumn Glory', H.'Autumn Beauty', H.'Autumn Blue'

(4.5 cm) in length, crowd the ends of the branchlets, in August and September.

A fairly hardy shrub which is a useful addition to any garden at all times of the year, with its foliage colour, flowers and appearance. Zone 9.

H.'Avalon'

A seedling that appeared in 1982 at Polden Acres, Somerset, a cross between H.'Miss E. Fittall' and H.'C.P. Raffill'.

An upright, much branched, close growing shrub; the stems light brown in colour, with darker brown nodes. Rounded in outline, growing to 4 ft 6 in (135 cm) in height. The leaves are narrow lanceolate; length up to 2½ in (6.5 cm); width ½ in (1.25 cm). They tend to be yellow green in colour. Pale purplish mauve flowers on cylindrical spikes, up to 3 in (7.5 cm) long, appear in summer.

A dainty flowered background shrub. Zone 10, or could be lower in protected borders.

H.'Baby Marie'

The origin of this hybrid is not known, but it was named by County Park Nursery in Essex. A neat rounded shrub growing to about 12–14 in (30–35 cm) in height, with reddish brown, close growing branchlets.

Small green leaves, closely arranged in four ranks up the stems, are angled upwards from the stem. The leaves are ovate; length ¼ in (6 mm); width ⅛ in (3 mm), paler beneath. The leaf bud has a narrow sinus. The flowers are mainly terminal, sessile, pale lilac, in early May. The spike is ½ in (1.25 cm) long, with two pairs of flowers at the base and single flowers opposite and alternate up the spike.

A plant for rock gardens or troughs. Zone 10, or could be slightly lower in sheltered gardens as plant can be damaged by severe frosts.

H.'Balfouriana'

This cultivar was raised at Edinburgh Botanic Gardens from seed sent from New Zealand, prior to 1897 when it was described in the *Botanical Magazine* of that year. It was named in honour of Sir Isaac Bayley Balfour (1850–1926), who was then Director of the Botanic Gardens. The parentage of this hybrid is not known.

Erect growing, rounded and not spreading, it grows to about 3 ft (90 cm), with purple branches ageing brown. The leaves are pale shining green, edged purple at first, ovate in shape; length ½–¾ in (1.25–1.8 cm); width ¼ in (6 mm). Pale purplish blue flowers, crowded in racemes 2–3 in (5–7.5 cm) long, appear near the top of the branches, in June and July. A hardy and pleasant shrub for the garden border. Zone 8.

H.barkeri

S.D. Barker, after whom this Hebe was named, collected plants in Westland, South Island, NZ and Chatham Islands, where this species was found in 1898.

An erect, stout shrub with upright branching, which grows happily by the sea. The stems are green, becoming purplish later. The leaves are apple green, spreading, paler beneath; length about 2 in (5 cm); width ¼ in (6 mm), either lanceolate or oblong lanceolate in shape. The leaf blade is covered with very fine hairs at first. Where the leaf joins the stem, there is a purple ring. Crowded racemes of flowers, up to 2 in (5 cm) long, appear towards the ends of the shoots, in summer. White in colour to stained purple.

A shrub to protect the coastal garden, growing up to 54 in (137 cm) or more in height. Zone 10.

H.'Barnettii'

Named after M.J. Barnett, MBE, a previous Director of Botanic Garden, Parks and Reserves, Christchurch, South Island, NZ.

A much branched plant with close set leaves growing to about 9 in (23 cm) in height. The leaves are grey green, glaucous, lanceolate; length ½ in (1.25 cm); width up to ¼ in (6 mm). Short spikes of white flowers are carried near the ends of the stems, in late spring. The spikes are about the same length as the leaves.

A compact cultivar for the rock garden. Zone 8 or lower.

H.'Beatrice'

A seedling from H.'Bowles' Hybrid' raised at County Park Nursery, Essex. The other parent is not known.

Upright, growing to about 2 ft (60 cm) in height. The leaves are shiny green, duller below, narrow lanceolate; length up to 1 in (2.5 cm); width ⁷⁄₁₀ in (5 mm). The stems are greeny brown at first with dark brown nodes where the almost stalkless leaves join. Because of early opening, it is difficult to see the growth bud at the end of the stem. Long narrow spikes of white flowers, 4 in (10 cm) long, cover the bushes in early summer.

Worth finding a space for this cultivar in the shrub border. Zone 10; could be lower in sheltered gardens.

H.benthamii

A stout woody shrub, named after George Bentham FRS (1800–1884), the distinguished English botanist. Found in rocky places on Campbell Island and Lord Auckland's Island, off NZ.

Variable in height from 6–30 in (15–75 cm), the down turning leaves are more numerous at the ends of the branchlets. They are variable in shape and size, elliptic oblong to spathulate depending on whether this shrub is growing on the mountain or at lower levels; length varies from ½–2 in (1.25–5 cm); width from ¼–½ in (0.6–1.25 cm). The leaves can be bluntly toothed with rounded edges and show white with matted soft hairs. Bright blue flowers are carried in a terminal raceme, tending to be crowded, in early summer.

Something different for the rock garden. Zone 7.

H.'Bicolor Wand'

One of the race of hardy hybrids bred by Treseders of Truro, Cornwall from H.'Miss E. Fittall'.

A large rounded shrub growing to 5 ft (150 cm) or more the stems are light brown with darker nodes. The leaves are narrow lanceolate, slightly irregular and narrowing to the tip. The leaf blade is dark green in colour, paler below; length 3½ in (9 cm); width up to ½ in (1.25 cm). The flowers are bluey purple, white at the base, displayed in 6 in (15 cm) long and up to 1 in (2.5 cm) diameter spikes in summer.

Useful for the back of the border. Zone 9 in sheltered areas, otherwise Zone 10 as this fine cultivar is slightly less hardy.

H.'Biggarii' (IS)

Named after George Biggar, who accompanied D.L. Poppelwell on his botanical expeditions. As yet it has not been decided whether this is a species or a hybrid. It is a plant of prostrate habit, found by Poppelwell on Eyre Mts, Otago, South Island, NZ at over 3,800 ft (1,158 m) amongst sub alpine rocks. The branches are 8–10 in (20–25 cm) long and are decumbent. The glaucous green leaves are oblong to oblong ovate, ½–¾ in (12–18 mm) long by up to ¼ in (6 mm) wide. Short rather dense racemes of small white flowers are carried on stiff, densely leaved branches, in early summer.

Zone 7, or lower.

H. × 'Bishopiana'

A natural hybrid from the rocky outcrops between Huia Hill and Little Huia near Manukau, North Island, NZ. A cross between H.obtusata and H.stricta. A low growing shrub, possibly up to 24 in (60 cm), found straggling over rocks with slender dark purple stems. Named after J.J. Bishop around 1924. The leaves are narrow lanceolate elliptic; length 2–3 in (5–7.5 cm); width ½ in (1.25 cm), green in colour. Lavender flowers, in spikes up to 4 in (10 cm) long, appear in late summer.

As far as is known, not yet grown in Britain. Zone 10.

H.'Bluebell'

A free flowering cultivar rather like a larger growing H.'Autumn Glory', possibly growing up to 3 ft (90 cm). The leaves are green, oval in shape; length 1½ in (4 cm); width ¾ in (2 cm). Short, stout racemes of deep purple flowers appear from midsummer to autumn, even up to October. Introduced by County Park Nursery of Essex as a good free flowering shrub.

Another shrub for the border; may need shelter. Zone 9/10.

H.'Blue Clouds'

A neat growing shrub, which originated as a seedling from H.'Mrs Winder' with purplish green branchlets. Raised at County Park Nursery, Essex. The leaves are dark green turning purplish green in winter, oblong ovate, blade spreading and down turning. The upper surface is shiny, duller and lighter green beneath; there is a slightly purplish central rib; length 1¾ in (4.5 cm); width ⅖ in (1 cm). Wisteria blue flowers on 2–3 in (5–7.5 cm) spikes begin appearing in June and there could be a flower or two on the bush in December.

A useful cultivar for flowers and foliage and worth finding a place for in the border. Not for the exposed garden. Zone 9.

H.'Blush Wand'

A tall growing, much branched shrub of the Wand Group of hybrids raised by Treseders of Truro, Cornwall from H.'Miss E. Fittall'.

Makes a rounded bush, 5–6 ft (150–180 cm) in height, with greeny brown stems with darker brown nodes. The leaves are mid green, lanceolate; length up to 3 in (7.5 cm); width ½ in (1.25 cm), with young leaves and main rib of the leaf suffused plum colour. Pale rose or blush pink flowers well fill the 6 in (15 cm) spikes that appear on the branches in summer.

A sturdy growing cultivar for the back of the border. Zone 9.

H.bollonsii

This species is named after J. Bollons, Captain of the survey ship which visited the islands around New Zealand. It is found in coastal scrub on Poor Knights Island and other islands like Hen and Chickens Island off North Island, NZ.

An erect growing shrub, with green branchlets that are finely pubescent, of medium growth up to 42 in (107 cm) or even more. The elliptic, upward growing leaves are glossy, mid to dark green and rather thickened and narrowing to the base; length 1¾–3 in (4.5–7.5 cm); width ½–1 in (1.25–2.5 cm). Racemes of purplish to white flowers, rather lax in their display, 2½–3½ in (6–9 cm), appear in mid- to late summer.

A coastal shrub, not hardy elsewhere. Zone 10.

H.'Boscawenii'

Named after Canon Boscawen of Ludgvan, near Penzance, Cornwall. An upright growing cultivar, yet semi-prostrate at the base. Origin is not known.

Growing to a height of 12–15 in (30–37 cm), the branchlets of this shrub are light brown in colour, with leaves close together at the base of the stem and wider apart near the top. The leaves are oblong in shape, shiny and mid green, narrowing to the tip. The lower leaves are ½ in (1.25 cm) in length and ⅕ in (5 mm) wide; the top leaves are ¼ in (6 mm) longer. The margins of the leaf blade are yellow green. The flowers are carried in two alternate pairs of racemes hiding the growing bud at the top of the stem. The light mauve flowers appear from early summer.

This shrub is a delight in coastal gardens; hardiness doubtful away from the coast or in exposed gardens. Zone 10.

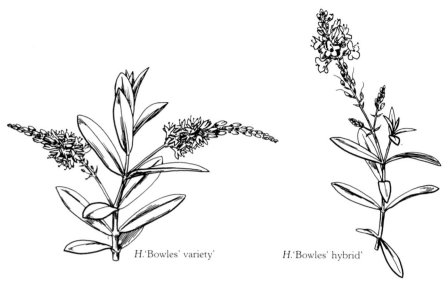

H.'Bowles' variety'   H.'Bowles' hybrid'

8.3 H. *'Bowles' Variety'*, H. *'Bowles' Hybrid'*

H.'Bowles' Hybrid'

This cultivar came from the garden of Warham Rectory and was described by the famous gardener, E.A. Bowles (1864–1954), in his book *My Garden in Summer.* A hybrid from *H.diosmifolia* with *H.parviflora* as possibly the other parent, producing a graceful rounded bush about 24 in (60 cm) in height. The stems are much branched, green, with a brown ring at the node where the leaves join. The leaves are pale green, slightly glossy, narrow, elliptic oblong; length about 1 in (2.5 cm); width ¼ in (6 mm) and upward growing. The lavender purple flowers are displayed in compound racemes with 2–5 branchlets, 3–4 in (7.5–10 cm) long, covering the bush from July to September.

It is a pity that this lovely cultivar is of doubtful hardiness in exposed gardens or where frosts can be severe, as it is well worth a place in any garden with its charming racemes of flowers which are well spaced and displayed. Zone 10.

H.'Bowles' Variety'

Little is known about this cultivar, which is quite different to *H*.'Bowles' Hybrid' and is hardier.

A neat, close growing shrub with branches tending to grow outward and upward, reaching about 18 in (45 cm) in height. The branchlets are brown in colour and the nodes a darker brown. The leaves are mid green, slightly shiny, ovate oblong in shape; length 1½ in (4 cm); width ⅖ in (1 cm) wide. There is a tendency for the leaves to turn face upward, yet the tips turn downwards and the central vein is depressed. The mauvy blue flowers are carried in cylindrical spikes, 3 in (7.5 cm) in length and up to ¾ in (1.8 cm) at the base and tapering to a point. The spikes, too, have a slight curve in them. The flowers appear from June on.

A useful cultivar for the garden, and hardy. Zone 9.

H.brachysiphon

(Latin — brachys = short, siphon = tube; refers to the corolla tube) Found in the Canterbury and Amuri districts and possibly extending to the mountains of Nelson, South Island, NZ. Introduced to Britain as *Veronica traversii*, but Sir J.D. Hooker found that the shorter corolla tube distinguished this plant from the true *V.traversii* and it was V.S. Summerhayes who gave this species the name of *H.brachysiphon*.

A slow growing, compact, semi-erect, rounded shrub, growing to 48–54 in (120–137 cm) in height with a spread of up to 48 in (120 cm). The branchlets are green with a brown nodal ring. The leaves are elliptic to lanceolate, mid green and duller below, possibly glaucous; length ½–1 in (1.25–2.5 cm); width ¼ in (6 mm). The leaf stalks (petioles) occasionally twist to make the leaves look as if they are in two ranks. The flowers are white, carried in short racemes ⅔ in (1.7 cm) long near the ends of the stems in late June. The racemes are in one or two pairs; the buds have a mauvy tint.

Often found growing as a barrier or hedge against the winds in coastal districts, such as on the Isles of Scilly. Zone 7.

H.brachysiphon 'White Gem'

The origin of this cultivar is not known and it is said to be from *H.brachysiphon*, but differs from it in some ways such as in height, up to 42 in (107 cm) or slightly more, it flowers earlier in mid June (in sheltered areas this could be even earlier), the leaves are more concave and the tip is not down turning. The branchlets are greeny brown, ageing light brown not dark brown as in *H.brachysiphon*.

The leaves are elliptic to slightly obovate; length ¾ in (2 cm), width ¼ in (6 mm). At colder times the tips yellow, extending to nearly half the leaf. The leaf margin is yellow and both surfaces of the blade are glossy. The flowers are carried in one or two pairs of short racemes, ¾ in (2 cm) in length. The buds do not have a mauvy tint; the flowers are white in colour.

Useful foliage plant for the border. Zone 7.

H.breviracemosa

(Latin — brevi = short, racemosus = raceme; meaning flowers arranged in a short raceme) Originated from the Kermadec Islands to the north of North Island, NZ (nearer the equator). Found on cliff ledges and rocky places inaccessible to goats, who have made this shrub an endangered species, and it now survives on Sunday Island.

A rather loosely branched shrub, with green branchlets on which are carried the spreading leaves; height 42–48 in (107–120 cm). The leaves are oblong lanceolate, shiny and with fine hairs around the margin; length

59

2–4 in (5–10 cm); width about 1 in (2.5 cm). The leaves have a tendency to become smaller below the racemes. The white to pale lilac small flowers are carried in quite short racemes, in early summer.

This shrub is frost tender. Zone 10.

H.'Brockiei' (IS)

Found in grassland at 3,800–4,900 ft (1,160–1,493 m) between Amuri Pass and Lake Man at the head of the Doubtful River, Canterbury, South Island, NZ. Named after W.B. Brockie, one time Curator of Otari Native Plant Museum, Wellington, NZ. Not yet recognised officially as a species, hence the (IS), but in the future it could be decided that it is a species.

A much branched, spreading plant, with green stems and similar in some ways to *H.pinguifolia* because of its low habit and leaf shape; height 8–12 in (20–30 cm). The leaves are deeply concave, broad, ovate, bright green, somewhat leathery; length c. ½ in (1–1.5 cm); width c. ¼ in (7–10 mm). Crowded racemes of white flowers, ¾–1½ in (2–4 cm) long, appear towards the end of May.

A hardy plant for rock gardens. Zone 7.

H.buchananii

A much branched shrub, decumbent to erect in growth, making low growing clumps on the drier eastern slopes of the Otago Mts and in the Southern Alps from Godley Valley southwards at an altitude of 3,000–5,000 ft (915–1,524 m). This species is named after J. Buchanan (1819–1898), the Scottish botanist, plant hunter and writer, who lived in New Zealand from 1849.

Low growing, up to 8 in (20 cm), and spreading in clumps up to 2–3 ft (60–90 cm) across. The branches are stout, almost black in colour, closely scarred and tortuous. The leaves are broadly ovate, ⅛–¼ in (3–6 mm) in both length and width, glaucous green, darker above but paler beneath. The white flowers are crowded in short spikes, ¾ in (2 cm) long, rather hidden in the foliage and pubescent. Flowers in late May or early June.

Quite hardy, attractive species for the rock garden or trough. In the sun it becomes more glaucous. Zone 7.

H.buchananii 'Minor'

A very compact form of *H.buchananii*, which see for details.

H.'Buxifolia'

In Britain there is a cultivar of this name, which is not recognised elsewhere, as it is said to be a form of *H.odora*. Until it is renamed, here is a brief description.

Upright, growing about 42 in (105 cm) in height. The branchlets are yellow green with small clusters of leaves or young branchlets at the ends. The leaves are ovate, fairly glossy, concave, yellow green; length ⅖ in (1 cm); width ⅛ in (3 mm), with yellow margins.

One very short terminal spike with two similar spikes in the first pair of leaf axils, forms a cluster of white flowers, in early summer.

A hardy foliage plant for the garden border. Zone 7.

H.'Buxifolia Nana'

An upright branching cultivar, with greeny brown stems, growing to about 8 in (20 cm) in height. Spreading in habit. The leaves are four ranked, elliptic obovate, shining above, paler beneath, with yellow green margins and slightly concave; length $\frac{2}{5}$ in (1 cm); width $\frac{1}{5}$ in (5 mm). White or pale lavender flowers, in short spikes, arise towards the ends of the branchlets, in early summer. At the ends of the branches there can be young branchlets arising in pairs.

A useful, low growing and spreading shrub for the front of the border or the rock garden. Zone 8 or Zone 9.

H.'Caledonia'

After much searching, the origin of this cultivar is still unknown, but it has been around for some time as it has acquired other names such as H.'E.B. Anderson', H.'Knightshayes' and H.'Percy Picton'.

It is an attractive dwarf shrub, rounded in outline and growing to a height of about 18 in (45 cm). The stems are reddish brown and upward growing. The leaves are green, often red edged, oblanceolate; length up to 1$\frac{1}{4}$ in (3 cm); width $\frac{3}{10}$ in) (8 mm) at the widest part of the leaf. Young leaves around the growth bud, as well as the bud itself, are tinged reddish brown, especially beneath the leaf. Terminal flower spikes, up to $\frac{1}{2}$ in (1.25 cm) long, appear at the end of the branchlets with 2–6 secondary spikes in the axils of the leaves from the ends of the branchlets. These secondary spikes can extend and then below their terminal spikes a further pair of spikes can appear. Spikes and leaves are opposite and alternate in four ranks. The violet flowers can appear from late spring to early autumn.

An ideal shrub for the border or the rock garden. Zone 9 or Zone 10, depending on the shelter of the site.

H.'Candy'

A seedling from H.albicans which was raised at County Park Nursery, Essex in 1978. It is pinkish flowered and strong growing; height over 2 ft (60 cm). Slightly less hardy than the parent. Zone 9.

H.canterburiensis

From the Canterbury Region, this low growing shrub can be found in tussock grassland from 3,000–4,000 ft (915–1,220 m) in the mountains from below Nelson to Arthur's Pass, South Island, NZ.

A fairly upright, low growing shrub, up to 8 in (20 cm) in gardens, but taller in the wild. The branchlets are green with a brown ring at the nodes; minutely hairy. The leaves are glossy green, obovate, densely arranged in one flat plane (distichous); length $\frac{1}{4}$–$\frac{1}{2}$ in (0.6–1.25 cm); width $\frac{1}{5}$ in (5 mm). White flowers, usually in pairs of spikes, 1 in (2.5 cm) long, appear at the end of the branchlets from late May.

An interesting plant for the rock garden, also found under the name of *H*.'Tom Marshall'. Zone 7; hardy.

8.4 H. canterburiensis, *showing leaves in one plane*

H.'Carl Teschner'

A synonym for *H*.'Youngii' which is the correct name, and see for details.

H.'Carnea'

A rounded, erect growing, narrow leaved Hebe, that arose in an unknown garden in New Zealand and was described by J.B. Armstrong in 1881 and by then it was well established. Although he named it as a species, there is no doubt that it is a hybrid with *H.speciosa* as one parent, hence its lack of hardiness.

A much branched, yet spreading shrub; height up to 4 ft (120 cm) or more. The branchlets are reddish brown. The leaves are linear oblong to linear lanceolate, shiny, light to mid green above, paler below; length 1½–2½ in (4–6.5 cm); width ½ in (1.25 cm). The flowers are distinct rosy purple fading to white so giving a two colour effect. Flower spikes, 3–3½ in (7.5–9 cm) long, appear near the ends of the branchlets in summer.

A good shrub for the warmer or sheltered garden. It is not a frost hardy cultivar. Zone 9 (10).

H.'Carnea Variegata'

The variegated form of H.'Carnea', origin unknown, with similar leaf shape, and colour of flowers. The branchlets have a slightly lighter reddish or purply brown colour with nodes of the darker colour of the parent stems. The leaves are variegated, grey green with cream margins and tips, and become tinged with rose in autumn. The leaf length and width is the same or slightly less than those for H.'Carnea'.

A cultivar for frost free areas or for bedding out in summer. Zone 10.

H.'Carnosula' (IS)

(Latin — carnosus = somewhat fleshy; refers to the leaves) This is one of the glaucous foliaged Hebes of the H.pinguifolia complex of the Nelson Mts, South Island, NZ. As yet it has not been decided whether it is a hybrid or a species, hence the (IS) indicating an uncertain species.

The branches are spreading and ascending, green when young, ageing brown; height 16 in (40 cm). The leaves are thick and fleshy, concave, broadly obovate, with the margins lighter green, remainder of the leaf blade glaucous green; length ⅖ in (1 cm); width ¼ in (6 mm). The leaf bud has a distinct sinus. Two rounded spikes, ½ in (1.25 cm) in diameter, appear just below the growing bud at the ends of the shoots, in June. The flowers are white, with purple anthers.

A popular, hardy garden plant for rock garden or border. Zone 7.

H.'Cassinioides'

(Latin — cassinioides = like a Cassinia) A plant, said to come from the Takitimu Mts in Southland, South Island, NZ, was cultivated in the garden of H.J. Matthews in Dunedin and was possibly a cross between the small leaved H.'Buxifolia' (now a form of H.odora) and the whipcord H.lycopodioides. A New Zealand plant which may or may not have reached Britain. Hardy, Zone 8.

H.chathamica

A small rambling shrub coming, as the name suggests, from the Chatham Islands, 500 miles (805 km) to the east of Christchurch, South Island, NZ, and found growing on the rocks and cliffs close to the sea, where there is plenty of spray.

Prostrate, rather wide spreading, growing to 4 in (10 cm) or possibly to 12 in (30 cm). The branchlets are slender. The leaves are spreading and inclined to one plane. The leaf blade is elliptic oblong, glabrous green above and paler beneath; length ½–1¼ in (1.25–3 cm); width ¾–½ in (6–12.5 mm). The flowers are predominantly white, but the tips of the petals are violet at first and soon fade to white. They appear in squat, dense flowered racemes, 1½ in (4 cm) long, in early summer.

A shrub for the coastal garden. It is reluctant to flower in Britain. Easy to propagate as the trailing branches layer themselves. Zone 9 or Zone 10.

H.cheesemanii

A much branched, whipcord like shrub named after the NZ botanist, T.F. Cheeseman (1846–1923), and found amongst rocks on the drier, eastern side of the South Island above Mt. Alta.

Rather upright growing and twiggy, up to 12 in (30 cm) in height. As in most whipcords, the leaves are very small, 1/12 in (2 mm) broadly ovate, close pressed to the branchlets in four ranks, green in colour. The flowers are white in colour and very small, and usually appear in two pairs at the ends of the branchlets, in summer.

Zone 7; hardy.

H.'Christabel'

A small, low growing whipcord hybrid, similar in habit to *H.subsimilis*, collected by Graham Hutchins by the shore of Lake Christabel, South Island, NZ. This semi-whipcord is bright geeen in colour and hardy.

H.'Christensenii'

Named after C.E. Christensen, who was the Tourist Agent at Hanmer Springs, South Island, NZ, and helped Dr L. Cockayne with his plant collection in the Hanmer District. This is a natural hybrid between almost certainly *H.odora* and a whipcord species. Although not a whipcord it fits in well with this group.

A rounded, fairly erect, much branched shrub, with the branches stout and green in colour, growing to about 3 ft (90 cm) in height. The leaves are erect to slightly spreading, dark green; length 1/8–3/16 in (3–5 mm); width up to 1/8 in (3 mm), with an ovate leaf blade which is concave and shiny, but paler beneath. The flowers are almost non-existent; a very shy flowerer.

Hardy; grown in many gardens in South Island, NZ. An attractive rounded or ball like shrub its dark green leaves show off the gold or yellow green branches of the whipcord Hebes. Zone 8.

H.ciliolata

(Latin — ciliate = fringed with hair, refers to the hairs along the margins of the leaves and bracts) This species is found at 4,000–6,000 ft (1,200–1,830 m) on the slopes above Browning's Pass, South Island, NZ, as well as in the Nelson Mts.

A loosely cushioning shrub, growing up to 12 in (30 cm) in height. The leaves are very small, narrow oblong, upright at first but spreading later; length 3/16 in (4 mm); width 1/16 in (1 mm), green in colour or yellow green. The white flowers, 1–3 pairs, are contained in a spike 1/4 in (6 mm) long; a very shy flowerer.

Hardy; a plant for planting among rocks. Zone 7.

H.coarctata

(Latin — coarctata = pressed together; refers to the branchlets being forced to grow on the upper sides of the arching branches) A whipcord species found in subalpine grassland from NW Nelson to the Bonner Range, South Island, NZ.

This whipcord shrub, with many arching branches, grows to about 30 in (75 cm), sometimes a little higher. The branchlets are shiny with well marked nodes. The leaves are small, deltoid and pressed to the stems; yellow green in colour; length $\frac{1}{12}$ in (2mm) and nearly as wide; joined at the base and up to half the length. White flowers are carried in short spikes of up to 12 flowers, in summer.

Hardy. Zone 7.

H.cockayniana

Named in honour of Dr L. Cockayne (1855–1934), the botanist and writer on NZ native plants and founder of the Otari Native Plant Museum at Wellington, North Island, NZ. This species is found in the Humbolt Mountains, near Lake Wakitipu, South Island, amongst the subalpine scrub and grassland at an altitude of 3,675 ft (1,120 m).

An erect, much branched shrub growing to about 36 in (90 cm) in height. The branchlets are rather stout with some hairs. The leaves are elliptic to oblong, shiny, but glaucous below with a prominent midrib; length $\frac{2}{5}$–$\frac{7}{10}$ in (1–1.7 cm); width $\frac{1}{4}$ in (6 mm). The leaf bud has a narrow sinus. White flowers, in the axils of the leaves, are carried towards the top of the branchlets, in spikes 1 in (2.5 cm) long, in early to mid-summer.

A hardy border shrub, with spreading green leaves. Zone 7.

H.colensoi

Named after W. Colenso (1811–1899), a botanist and writer. This species grows on cliffs above river valleys at an altitude of 1,500–3,000 ft (460–915 m), from Taruarau River to the northern Ruahine Range, North Island, NZ.

Low growing, rather open yet bushy, growing up to 18 in (45 cm), sometimes a little higher. The leaves are obovate, thick and glossy on both surfaces and upward pointing; length $\frac{3}{4}$–$1\frac{1}{8}$ in (2–2.7 cm); width $\frac{2}{5}$ in (1 cm). Glaucous green in colour, both leaves and stems, which have brown nodal rings. The leaf bud has a sinus. White flowers are carried in racemes towards the ends, or at the ends, of the stems, in summer.

A useful plant that will grow in sun or shade and is an ideal small shrub for the rock garden. Zone. 7.

H.colensoi var. glauca

A variety of H.colensoi with waxy, glaucous, grey green leaves. A compact form for rock gardens and troughs. For further details see H.colensoi.

H.'Colwall'

Has been described as a more erect form of H.'Youngii', which was one of its parents. It was raised at Ballard Nursery, Colwall, near Malvern, Worcestershire.

Semi-erect, rather loosely spreading, this species grows up to 12 in (30 cm) or slightly higher. The stems are reddish brown near the tips, turning green and finally brown. The nodes, where the leaves join, are darker and tend to stand out. The leaves are upward growing except at the ends of the stem, elliptic ovate and dark green; length ½ in (1.25 cm); width ³⁄₁₆ in (4 mm); The margins of the leaves can be reddish when young. Short spikes of cyclamen purple flowers, up to ¾ in (2 cm) in length, appear from mid June and sometimes earlier.

A pretty rock garden plant, when in flower. Zone 9.

H.'Cookiana'

Although in cultivation in England, the botanical differences are too slight for making this a recognised form of *H.stricta* (see *H.stricta* var. *macroura* for full details). It was found on the cliffs and by the seaside of Table Cape, Cook District, North Island in 1887 by Mr H. Hill and indirectly honours Captain Cook in the name.

H.corriganii

This species was found by Mr D.H.L. Corrigan at McLaren's Falls, Tauranga, North Island, NZ.

A branching shrub with stout branchlets, 5 ft (150 cm) tall or higher. The leaves can be up to 3 in (7.5 cm) in length and 1 in (2.5 cm) in width, abruptly narrowing into the stalk, but evenly tapered to the tip of the leaf blade, which is green and glabrous. The leaf is described as linear lanceolate. The leaf bud has a noticeable sinus. White or pale lilac flowers in spikes, up to the length of the leaves, appear near or at the ends of the shoots, in spring or early summer.

A shrub akin to *H.salicifolia* in growth. Zone 10.

H.'County Park'

This cultivar is a seedling from *H.pimeleoides* var. *glaucocaerulea* and was raised at County Park Nursery, Essex.

A spreading plant, up to 18 in (45 cm) across, the branchlets tend to be decumbent; height 8 in (20 cm). The leaves are grey green with a red edge, but in winter cold spells the upper surface becomes suffused with pinkish mauve. The leaf bud has a small sinus; the leaf blade is ovate; length ½ in (1.25 cm); width ¼ in (6 mm). Short spikes of violet flowers 1 in (2.5 cm) in length, appear towards the ends of the shoots in June and July.

A very good ground cover plant. Zone 8.

H.'C.P. Raffill'

This cultivar grew up in a stock bed of *H.*'Spender's Seedling' in a West Sussex Nursery; because it was rather similar to its parent it was difficult to isolate. J. Souster recognised this taller growing cultivar, described and named it 'C.P. Raffill' after his Curator at Kew.

Much branched, upright growing yet rounded in outline, in gardens, a height of 5 ft (150 cm) is reached. The slender stems are green becoming greeny brown, with brown nodes. The leaves are narrow lanceolate, spreading; length to 2½ in (6.5 cm); width ²⁄₁₀ in (5 mm). The leaf blades are down turning towards the tip, dull green in colour with a slightly lighter midrib. Some leaves appear sickle shaped due to the turning of the tip. White flowers are carried in narrow spikes, ¼ in (6 mm) in diameter by 2½ in (6.5 cm) in length. The stalk can add a further inch (2.5 cm). The flowers appear in June and again later.

A hardy cultivar for the back of the border with its showy spikes of flowers. Zone 8.

H.'Cranleighensis'

Although this shrub is named after Cranleigh in Surrey, who gave it that name is not known.

A rather lax shrub with browny green stems, growing up to 30 in (75 cm). The leaves are dark green, narrow lanceolate 2¼ in (6 cm) long and ½ in (1.25 cm) wide. The leaf blade is slightly shiny but paler below. The leaves are plum coloured at first on the under side, but as they grow only the midrib retains the plum colour. The pink flowers are carried in 2½ in (6.5 cm) spikes in the axils of the leaves at the ends of the stems, in summer.

A pleasant shrub for the protected or frost free garden. Zone 10.

H.'Cranleigh Gem'

A cultivar from *H.albicans* growing to a height of about 24 in (60 cm); origin not known.

A much branched, rounded shrub, compact rather than spreading. The stems are greeny brown at first then brown later. The leaves are grey, glaucous, ovate, narrowing at the stem end, more rounded at the tip; length up to ¾ in (2 cm); width ¼ in (6 mm). Short, fairly crowded spikes of white flowers, with brown anthers, appear from June on.

A useful hardy shrub for the border. Zone 7.

H.cupressoides

This cupressus like whipcord Hebe was found east of the main divide from Marlborough to the Otago Lakes, South Island, NZ on river flats and terraces up to 4,900 ft (1,500 m), but over recent years has become more localised and not so common.

Densely branched, forming a symmetrically rounded bush, the branchlets are close set and flexible as well as being glaucous; height up to 54 in (137 cm), erect growing. The fleshy green leaves are very small, triangular, rounded and close pressed to the stem; length ¹⁄₁₂ in (2 mm) long. Six–eight bluish purple flowers appear near the ends of the branchlets, in early summer. There is a little reluctance to flower at first, but when an older plant flowers the whole bush appears to be covered in a blue mist.

This hardy bluish green shrub can be the ideal alternative to the conifer in the garden. Zone 7.

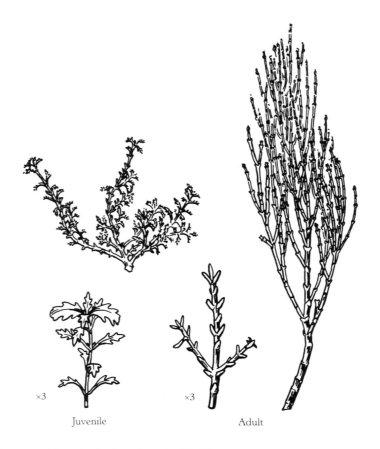

×3   ×3

Juvenile   Adult

8.5 H.cupressoides, *showing juvenile and adult foliage*

H.cupressoides 'Boughton Dome'

Introduced by Lady Scott and named after Boughton House, Northamptonshire. This is a dwarfer form of *H.cupressoides* growing to about 18 in (45 cm) in height.

More rounded than the parent, retaining more of the juvenile foliage, this shrub has a more feathery appearance, and is densely branched with close set branchlets. The juvenile leaves are fleshy with two, four or even six lobes, outward spreading from the glaucous green branchlets which at first have a grey green look caused by fine, small soft hairs; length up to ¼ in (6 mm); width ¹⁄₁₂ in (2 mm). The adult leaves are very small, triangular and pressed to the stem, as in the parent. Six–eight bluish purple flowers appear near the ends of the branchlets, in late May or June.

A good shrub for the smaller garden and an alternative to a conifer in planting schemes. Zone 7.

H.cupressoides nana

A greener, less glaucous form of *H.cupressoides* growing to about 30 in (75 cm) in height. Rounded appearance. a little wider and slightly less erect. Hardy. Zone 7.

H.'Dartonii'

A Hebe collected, grown and named by H.L. Darton in 1922. It came from the rocky banks of the Clutha River, Otago District, South Island, NZ and was a *H.salicifolia* hybrid. Grows to about 54 in (135 cm). The leaves are lanceolate up to 1 in (2.5 cm) in length and ⅖ in (1 cm) in width. This used to be grown widely in New Zealand, but is probably not grown in Britain. White flowers in spikes, 1¾–2¼ in (4–6 cm) long, form at the ends of the branchlets in early to midsummer.

H.'Darwiniana' (IS)

From the interior hills, Hawke's Bay, North Island, NZ with such very slight botanical differences from *H.glaucophylla* from South Island that it is now included in that species. It remains a plant of uncertain status (IS). (See *H.glaucophylla* for details).

H.decumbens

(Latin — decumbens = lying down. Those plants whose branches trail across the ground, with the ends of the shoots tending to rise, are said to be decumbent) This small, spreading shrub can be found in the subalpine scrub and rocks in the mountains of Marlborough, North Canterbury and Nelson, South Island, NZ.

Grows to a height of 18 in (45 cm), with rather slender, dark purple or purplish brown, shiny, branchlets. The leaves are spreading, small, elliptic in shape and yellow green to dark green, with distinct reddish margins when growing in the sun; length up to ⅗ in (1.5 cm); width of leaf blade ¼ in (6 mm). White, almost sessile, flowers, in spikes ¾–1 in (2–2.5 cm) long, appear towards the ends of the branchlets, in summer.

A hardy species for the rock garden, the white flowers help set off the foliage. Has been found with the cultivar name of 'Robin' in Britain. Zone 7.

H.'Diamond'

A rounded, fairly tall and spreading cultivar possibly from Guernsey, Channel Islands, but also growing in Jersey.

Grows to a height of 54 in (137 cm), fairly well branched; the branchlets are light browny green with darker nodes. The leaves are elliptic ovate; length 3 in (7.5 cm); width up to 1 in (2.5 cm). The leaf blade is dark green, shiny and paler beneath with a plum coloured midrib. Showy spikes of purple flowers, which fade lighter to give a two colour effect, 3–4 in (7.5–10 cm) long and 1 in (2.5 cm) across, appear in summer.

A showy shrub for the border in the warmer garden. Zone 10.

H.'Diana'

A hybrid between H.'Miss E. Fittall' and H.'Great Orme' which arose in Polden Acres Garden, Edington, Somerset in 1981.

Upright, nicely branched and rounded in outline, the stems are green ageing brown. Grows to a height of 54 in (137 cm). The leaves are lanceolate up to 3 in (7.5 cm) and ¾ in (2 cm) wide. Green in colour, slightly shiny but paler beneath. There is a vein patterning on the leaf blade. Attractive lilac purple flowers are carried on narrow 4 in (10 cm) spikes not only in summer but in autumn as well. The spikes arise towards the ends of the branchlets.

Its full potential as an attractive shrub for the border is now coming to be recognised. In a sheltered situation and out of cold, piercing winds it could be a little hardier. Zone 10.

H.dieffenbachii

This species from the Chatham Islands off the east coast of South Island, NZ is named after E. Dieffenbach (1811–1855), a plant collector, who was born in Germany.

This is a fairly stout shrub, wide spreading up to 4 ft (120 cm) or more, with glabrous to hoary branchlets, pale green in colour. In a coastal position, it will grow over walls or banks or down cliffs, but it can grow more upright, with a little training in coastal gardens. H.barkeri is a near relation but differs in growing more upright and the leaves have fine hairs on both upper and lower surfaces. The leaves are fleshy, pale green, elliptic oblong; length 2–3½ in (5–9 cm); width up to 1 in (2.5 cm). Dull upper surface, paler beneath. The leaves are mostly spreading. Purplish to white flowers, in spikes about the same length as the leaves, appear in summer.

A very useful coastal shrub as it will grow in most soils and in either sun or shade. Zone 9.

H.'Dilatata' (IS)

(Latin — dilato = to spread out) as does this shrub in mats up to 39 in (1 m) in diameter on the debris slopes near Blue Lake on the Garvie Mts, Otago, South Island, NZ. Not recognised, as a distinct species because of its likeness to H.'Biggarii' (IS).

A prostrate, much branched shrub, growing up to 12 in (30 cm) or more in height. The branchlets are purple at first then green later. The leaves are obovate oblong, pale green and somewhat fleshy; length up to ½ in (1.25 cm); width ¼ in (6 mm). In the wild or in the garden the inflorescences or flower spikes are poorly formed and the white flowers often fail to develop.

A mountain shrub growing at an altitude of 4,500 ft (1,370 m). Zone 7.

H.diosmifolia

(Latin — diosmifolia = like the foliage of a diosma) Found by A. Cunningham, from North Kaipara Head and Whangarei northwards in North Island, NZ.

A low growing shrub, much branched, spreading, with slender branchlets, growing up to 4 ft (120 cm) or even more. The leaves are obovate to lanceolate, dark green, lighter below; length ½–1⅛ in (1.5–2.7 cm); width ⅛–¼ in (3–6 mm). The flowers open heliotrope and fade white, thus giving a misty effect to the crowded corymbs of flowers that form at the ends of the branchlets through spring.

An attractive species for the warmer, sheltered garden. It responds to being planted in the sun. Zone 10.

H.diosmifolia 'Wairua Beauty'

A larger form of H.diosmifolia, originally found by the Wairua Falls, Titoki, near Whangarei, North Island, NZ. It is grown in gardens around Auckland, NZ and, with its larger corymbs of heliotrope flowers and flowering over four weeks, this is an outstanding cultivar for the warmer North Island. Other differences are that the leaves are pale or yellowish green and up to 1 in (2.5 cm) long. Zone 10.

H.divaricata

(Latin — divaricatus = spreading irregularly) An erect growing shrub found in forests, along streamsides and in rocky places in the Nelson and Marlborough Regions, South Island, NZ.

An upright growing, much branched shrub, can be spreading including the yellow green branchlets. Plants from the Pelorus Valley, Marlborough, are more compact and grow to 3–4 ft (90–120 cm), but plants from other areas can grow up to 8–9 ft (245–275 cm) and are more spreading. The leaves are narrow lanceolate, glabrous green, slightly shiny on the upper surface, but paler below; length ¾–1¼ in (2–3 cm); width ⅛–⅕ in (3–5 mm). The leaf bud has a long narrow sinus. The compound, much branched racemes of loosely spaced white flowers crowd the ends of the branchlets just below the growing bud, which they overtop, producing a mass of foamy white flowers, in early summer.

This shrub grows well in shade. Although a very showy shrub, when in flower, it seems to have been neglected for more colourful shrubs. Zone 8 or Zone 9.

H.'Divergens'

This plant is a natural hybrid collected from Brighton, south of Westport, South Island, NZ. It is said that H.elliptica could be one parent. The plant grows to about 1 ft (30 cm).

In Latin, divergens implies that the growths spread outward from the base and in this case produce a small rounded shrub with upward pointing leaves and branchlets to give a rather spiky appearance. The branchlets are greeny brown, with darker brown nodes. The leaves are grey, glaucous

71

and with green margins. The leaf blade is dark green, elliptic, covered with grey hairs, very fine and downy; length up to 1 in (25 mm); width ³/₁₀ in (8 mm). Pale lilac or white flowers, in short spikes a little shorter than the leaves, appear in summer towards the ends of the shoots. Violet anthers are an attraction.

A good rock garden plant. Zone 8.

H.'Dorothy Peach'

A cultivar that could be described as a smaller form of H.'Watson's Pink', but who raised it or after whom it is named has not been found.

It grows up to 42 in (105 cm), is fairly erect and neat in habit with greeny brown branches. The leaves are oblong elliptic, spreading and mainly down turning, with some overlapping as they are closely set; length up to 2 in (5 cm); width ²/₅ in (1 cm). Green, slightly shiny, paler and not so shiny beneath. The light pink flowers are displayed on spikes up to 2 in (5 cm) long with ½ in (1.25 cm) stalks towards the ends of the stems, in summer.

A useful cultivar for the smaller garden shrub border. Zone 10, or in sheltered coastal gardens.

H.'Douglasii'

Referred to in the 1926 catalogue of Duncan & Davies, New Plymouth, NZ, but there was no description. A plant of hybrid origin and could be from H.colensoi.

The branches radiate out from the base at an angle of 45°, they are light brown in colour and darker at the nodes. The leaves are mid green in colour with a lighter green edge, leaf blade glossy, duller below, oval to ovate, fleshy, and concave; length ¾ in (2 cm); width ³/₁₀ in (8 mm). The leaves tend to overlap and arise at the same angle as the branches. The white flowers, in short spikes ½ in (1.25 cm) long and ⅕ in (5 mm) in width, appear in summer.

A plant for the alpine enthusiast. Zone 7.

H.'Edinensis'

This hybrid originated at the Edinburgh Botanic Garden and was said to be between H.hectori and H.pimeleoides. Since 1904 it has become very popular as a rock garden plant, but today there is still doubt concerning one parent, namely H.pimeleoides.

Low growing and decumbent; as the branches spread so the green branchlets tend to grow upwards, making a shrub 9–12 in (22.5–30 cm) in height and 15–18 in (37–75 cm) across. The leaves are small, narrow lanceolate, clasping the stem for half their length then spreading outward, dark green slightly shiny, paler below; length ¼ in (6 mm); width ¹/₁₀ in (2 mm). Pale blue to white flowers appear at the ends of the shoots, in summer.

An attractive edge of border or rock garden plant with its whipcord like growth. Zone 7.

H.'Edington'

In 1975 a seedling grew between H.'Midsummer Beauty' and H.'Autumn Glory' at Polden Acres Gardens, and was found to be a hybrid of these two cultivars. It was named Edington after the Somerset village in which it was growing.

A fairly erect, yet rounded shrub with bronze stems and darker nodes; height 42 in (105 cm). The leaves are oblong lanceolate, dark green, paler beneath, midrib bronzed; length up to 2½ in (6.5 cm); width ⅗ in (1.5 cm). Bright purple flowers, on spikes 3½–4 in (9–10 cm) long, appear from late May to early October.

A shrub to be grown for its flowers, ideal for the border. Zone 8, except in exposed gardens where it is Zone 9.

H.elliptica (NZ)

A rather variable species frequenting the shorelines and coast of North Island from Mt. Taranaki (Egmont) southward and from Golden Bay down the west coast of South Island to Fiordland then the coasts of Southland and up the east coast as far as Otago, NZ. (See Appendix 1)

A much branched, bushy shrub growing to a height of 5 ft (150 cm) or more. The young branchlets are green in colour with larger leaves at the lower end. The leaves are dark green, shiny, paler beneath. The leaf blade is elliptic to elliptic oblong or occasionally obovate oblong, coming to a point, inclined to be fleshy; length varies from ¾–1½ in (2–4 cm); width up to ⅖ in (1 cm). The large flowers are mainly white, but can have shades of mauve or violet in the petals. They are displayed in spikes, consisting of 4–14 flowers, close to the ends of the branches in late spring or early summer.

A useful coastal shrub not minding salt winds or spray. Rather shy to flower in Britain, but not in its native land. Zone 9 or Zone 10 away from the coast.

H.elliptica (Solander)

The Veronica decussata of Daniel Solander is found extensively on the Falkland Islands, where it grows in scrub like patches and is known as Box or Boxwood. Also grows on the coasts of Chile and Tierra del Fuego on the mainland of South America. (See Appeidix 1)

A much branched shrub growing on cliffs and along the coast, up to 60 in (150 cm) tall. Stems are light brown in colour, darker at the nodes and semi erect. Leaves are glossy green, paler below, with 2 serrations, occasionally 4, near the apex of some of the leaves. Leaf blade is obovate, rounded at the apex, ¾ in (2 cm) long and ⅖ in (1 cm) wide. The leaf stalk is very short. In summer the white flowers appear in terminal or lateral racemes towards the ends of the branches.

It is thought to be hardier than H.elliptica (NZ) which it is said to resemble botanically. A hardy Zone 8 shrub, possibly Zone 9 away from the coast.

H.elliptica var. *crassifolia*

Comes from the coast close to the base of Mt. Taranaki, North Island, NZ and also Kapiti Island.

A larger growing form with very stout branchlets. The leaves are oblong to broadly obovate, pale green, with a tendency to be fleshy; length 1¼ in (3 cm); width ⅗ in (1.5 cm). Large, white flowers, up to ¾ in (2 cm) across in spikes like the parent are carried at the ends of the stems in late spring or early summer.

Zone 10, or Zone 9 by the coast.

H.'Emerald Green'

(Synonymous — H.'Milmont Emerald' and H.'McKean') A neat growing semi whipcord hybrid found by Mr H. McKean in 1970 at an altitude of 4,000 ft (1,219 m) in Ruahine Mountains, North Island, NZ and possibly a cross between *H.subsimilis* and *H.odora*.

A cushion like, much branched, small shrub growing up to 12 in (30 cm). The branchlets are green and upward growing. The leaves are closely spaced, four ranked and at an angle of 45° to the stem; length up to ⅛ in (3 mm); width 1/12 in (1.5 mm). The leaf blade is shiny, dull beneath and the margin is yellow green. The whipcord parentage is evidenced by the plant having crenated juvenile foliage, as well as the entire (no crenations) adult foliage. Small white flowers are carried towards the ends of the branchlets, in summer.

Look no further for an interesting plant for small rockeries and troughs. Zone 8.

H.epacridea

(Epacridea is derived from the Greek — epi = upon, akros = summit, meaning growing upon the tops of hills) In this case upon the Mts of Nelson and Marlborough, South Island, NZ.

Rather straggly with some ascending, well leaved, woody stems. Low growing to a height of a few inches (cm). Mostly prostrate with the woody stems up to 8–12 in (20–30 cm) long. The leaves are very small, crowded and overlapping, in four rows. The leaf blade is leathery, with thickened edges, ovate, 3/16 in (4 mm). The margins can be reddened. The white flowers, are carried in a terminal spike, ½–1¼ in (1.5–3 cm) long, in May. The flowers are crowded except in lower lateral spikelets of 2–4 flowers.

An alpine plant related to *H.haastii* from the west or wetter side of the Southern Alps. Zone 7.

H.'Ettrick Shepherd'

James Hogg was both poet and Ettrick shepherd and after him this cultivar is named. Nothing can be found about its origin.

A neat, rounded shrub growing to a height of up to 54 in (135 cm), much branched with slender, greeny brown branchlets carrying plum coloured growth buds. The leaves are oblanceolate, mid green; length 2½ in (6.5 cm); width ⅖ in (1 cm). The ribs beneath young leaves are plum coloured. The flowers are magenta purple at first fading to white, and are densely packed in spikes 3–4 in (7.5–10 cm) long, appearing in July towards the ends of the stems.

An unpretentious cultivar for the shrub border, but attractive in flower. Zone 9 to Zone 10.

H.evenosa

A shrub with stout, spreading main branches from the Tararua Range, North Island, NZ. The branchlets, too, are fairly stout and subdividing below the leafy tips. The leaves are mat green, slightly spreading yet upright growing; length ½–¾ in (1.25–2 cm); width ¼ in (6 mm). The leaf blade is obovate oblong, duller below. White flowers in short spikes 1–1¼ in (2.5–3 cm) in length appear in summer.

Not a widely cultivated shrub. Zone 8.

H.'Eveline'

Introduced by Caledonia Nursery, Guernsey, Channel Islands, late in the nineteenth century. In the 1920s, this Hebe was sent to England, where it became H.'Gauntlettii'. Today H.'Eveline' is still being grown in Guernsey.

A compact, well branched, rounded shrub growing up to 54 in (135 cm). The green stems well display the leaves, which are green, shiny but paler below. The leaf blade is lanceolate or oblanceolate; length 2½ in (6.5 cm); width ⅘ in (2 cm). Deep purple pink flowers are carried on long spikes, 5–6 in (12.5–15 cm), in August and September.

A showy cultivar by whichever name you know it. Zone 10.

H. 'Eveline'

H. 'Evelyn'

8.6 H.'Eveline', H.'Evelyn'

H.'Evelyn'

Not to be confused with the previous cultivar. This Hebe was introduced by Messrs R.W. Wallace of Tunbridge Wells, Kent. The origin of this cultivar is not known.

A rounded, well branched shrub with green stems and a brown ring at the nodes; height up to 54 in (135 cm). The leaves are green in colour, oblanceolate, with slight crenations and vein patterning and a lighter green margin; length 2–2¼ in (5–6 cm); width up to ⁷/₁₀ in (1.7 cm). Purply pink flowers, closely arranged in medium length spikes up to 2 in (5 cm) on long stalks, 1½ in (4 cm) long, appear from the end of June.

A cultivar for the shrub border. Zone 9, or could be lower in sheltered gardens.

H.'Eversley Seedling'

Efforts to find the origin of this hardy cultivar have so far failed, but whatever its origin it is an attractive Hebe.

Erect growing, yet spreading, much branched and rounded in outline; height and spread 42 in (105 cm). The branches are slender, brown, more reddish towards the tips. The young buds can also be suffused red brown. There are red brown margins to the green lanceolate leaves; length 1¼ in (3 cm); width ³/₁₀ in (8 mm) wide. Amethyst purple flowers are carried in spikes, 1½–3 in (4–7.5 cm). The main flowering periods are late May and early autumn, but some flowers can be found on the bushes throughout the year.

An attractive shrub for foliage and flowers and an added contrast in the shrub border, especially with grey foliaged shrubs. Zone 8 or even lower.

H.'Fairfieldii'

(× 'Fairfieldensis') Originated in Mr Martin's Nursery at Fairfield, near Dunedin, South Island, NZ, a cross between *H.hulkeana* and *H.lavaudiana* producing a stronger plant.

A sturdy, rather erect, well branched shrub; the branchlets are purplish in colour. Height up to 12 in (30 cm). The leaves are broadly ovate to oblong orbicular, narrowing to a channelled petiole. The leaf blade appears leathery, dark green, paler below; length ¾–1¼ in (2–3 cm); width up to ¾ in (2 cm). The leaf margins are crenate and reddish. Lavender violet flowers are carried in a broad terminal panicle, 6–9 in (15–22.5 cm) in length. The flowers are produced in fair quantity in early summer.

One of the most handsome Hebes to grow, in warmer gardens it can grow up to 36 in (90 cm). For the sake of its health, it pays to remove dead flowers straightaway. Zone 10 in coastal regions; Zone 9 in sheltered gardens.

H.'Fairlane'

Probably a cross between *H.*'Youngii' and *H.pinguifolia*, occurring at County Park Nursery in Essex.

A rounded spreading shrub, the branchlets brown with darker nodes and tending to grow upward to about 10 in (25 cm). The, leaves are green, slightly glaucous, with a lighter green margin which can be reddish on young leaves. The leaf blade is obovate, slightly concave and spreading, with a tendency to down turn; length ½ in (1.25 cm); width ¼ in (6 mm). The mauve flowers, in short racemes the same length as the leaves, are carried towards the ends of the stems, in June.

A rock garden or front of border plant. Zone 8 or Zone 9.

H.'Ferndown'

A seedling from H.'Jewel' found growing in a garden in Ferndown, Dorset and named after that place.

A rounded, semi erect shrub, growing up to 54 in (135 cm) with brown stems, darker at the nodes. The leaves are ovate oblong up to 3 in (7.5 cm) in length and ¾ in (2 cm) in width, channelling into the stalk, which is pressed against the stem when young. The leaf blade is green, paler below. Deep mauvy blue flowers are carried in spikes the same length as leaves, in June. Where it differs from H.'Jewel', mainly, is that it flowers again from September to December in mild autumns.

A useful border shrub with its two flowering times as well as its attractive flowers. Zone 9.

H.formosa

Introduced from Tasmania, SE Australia in 1835 and still called *Veronica formosa* in that country. There are few references to accurate descriptions of species that grow outside New Zealand or those details are hard to trace. It is said that H.'Girdwoodiana' is a garden synonym and this shrub can still be found growing in Guernsey.

An erect, much branched shrub growing up to 48 in (120 cm). The branchlets are green with a brown nodal ring. The leaves are oblong lanceolate, green, slightly shiny above and scarcely stalked; length ¾ in (2 cm); width ³/₁₆ in (4 mm). Lilac to purplish blue flowers in short spikes, 1 in (2.5 cm) long, but the spikes further towards the top of the stem are longer and can be twice the length; width of spikes ½ in (1.25 cm). Flowers in mid to late summer.

A tender species, this is a pretty shrub where it can be grown. Zone 10. (Much of this description is from RHS *Dictionary of Gardening*, 1951 — the shrub brought from Guernsey in 1975 as H.'Girwoodiana' fits this description except the leaves are twice as long and the top axillary spikes of flowers are 3 in (7.5 cm) long. The flower spikes tend to become fasciated at the tips.)

H. × 'Franciscana'

(*Veronica decussata* 'Devonia') As the origin will take much space to describe, refer to Appendix 1 for fuller details. Still found growing wild along coasts of Cornwall and Guernsey and used for shelter in the Isles of Scilly.

A much branched, compact growing shrub, rounded in outline growing up to 54 in (135 cm). The stems are greeny brown, darker at the nodes. The leaves are dark green, paler below, elliptic and obovate (on same bush); length up to 2¼ in (6 cm); width 1 in (2.5 cm) and tending to spread. Large, pinky purple flowers are carried in cylindrical spikes, 2½–3 in (6.5–7.5 cm) in length, summer and autumn flowering.

An ideal coastal shrub, but not hardy or happy inland. Zone 9 coastal; Zone 10 elsewhere.

H. × 'Franciscana Blue Gem'

(*Veronica lobelioides*) See Appendix 1 for origin. The most striking of the hybrids and is grown on sea fronts and coastal gardens.

Much branched and spreading, nearly as wide as high, growing to a height of 54 in (135 cm) or more. The branchlets are greeny brown with brown nodes. The dark green, glossy leaves are elliptic oblong or broad obovate; length varies from 1½–2½ in (4–6.5 cm); width from ¾–1 in (2–2.5 cm). Large violet blue flowers are carried in 2½ in (6.5 cm) spikes, in summer.

A showy shrub for coastal districts. Zone 9 by the sea; Zone 10 inland.

H. × 'Franciscana Lavender Queen'

H. × 'Franciscana' hybrid; how and where it arose is not known. A taller growing shrub, up to 60 in (150 cm).

An erect, branched and not so spreading shrub with a rather stiff appearance. The branchlets are light green, the leaves vary in size on the branchlets from 1–3 in (2.5–7.5 cm) in length and from ½–1 in (1.25–2.5 cm) in width. Both elliptic and oblanceolate leaf blades occur. The leaves are green to light green and at right angles to the stem, when fully grown. Lavender mauve flowers in medium length spikes, 2–2½ in (5–6.5 cm) long, appear in summer and autumn.

A good background shrub for the coastal garden border. Zone 9 in coastal areas; elsewhere Zone 10.

H. × 'Franciscana Sarnia'

This plant was noticed flowering in a garden at Les Vauxbelets, Guernsey in October 1975. It was said to be a chance seedling. Cuttings brought back to Polden Acres, Somerset for checking were rooted and it was found to be different from H. × 'Franciscana White Gem' and similar in growth and habit to H. × 'Franciscana', so it was decided to grow and name it. 'Sarnia' was chosen, the Roman name for Guernsey.

A well branched, fairly spreading, rounded shrub growing to 48 in (120 cm) in height or more. The leaves are dark green, elliptic and obovate; length up to 2 in (5 cm); width ¾ in (2 cm). White flowers in fairly broad, cylindrical spikes, up to 2 in (5 cm) in length, appear from July into autumn.

A coastal shrub with greeny brown stems with brown nodes. Zone 9 by the coast; Zone 10 inland.

H. × 'Franciscana Variegata'

The variegated form of H. × 'Franciscana', but where it originated has not been traced.

A well branched, rounded shrub not so large or spreading as H. × 'Franciscana' and growing up to 36 in (90 cm) at the most. The green stems have brown nodes. The leaves are elliptic and obovate up to 1¾ in (4.5 cm) in length and ¾ in (2 cm) in width. The yellow variegation around the margin of the leaf is irregular. Large, pinky purple flowers in cylindrical spikes, 2½ in (6.5. cm) long, appear in summer.

Shelter and sun are needed to get the best from this coastal shrub. Zone 9 by the coast, Zone 10 inland.

H. × 'Franciscana White Gem'

An albino form which Treseders of Truro, Cornwall discovered in a coastal garden in Cape Cornwall, near St Just, Cornwall. Dwarfer than H. × 'Franciscana Variegata' in size of leaves, flower spikes and growth. The flowers are pure white and appear in summer. Not hardy or happy away from the coast. Zone 10.

H.'Franjo'

Named after two schoolgirls, Frances and Joanna, who helped Graham Hutchins at County Park Nursery in Essex, where this cultivar was raised.

A neat rounded shrub with mauvy green stems, growing to about 24 in (60 cm) in height. The leaves are green, shiny and elliptic, ½ in (1.25 cm) long and ¼ in (6 mm) wide. Mauvy blue flowers, in racemes 1¼–2 in (3–5 cm) in length, appear in June and July.

A hardy free flowering shrub. Zone 8.

H.fruticeti

(Latin — fruticetum = growing in a thicket) The name refers to the subalpine scrub in which this species can be found, at the head of the Estuary Burn, Lake Wanaka, South Island, NZ. H.fruticeti is closely allied to H.subalpina, which has larger and wider leaves.

A closely branched, spreading shrub, up to 42 in (105 cm) in height. The branchlets are green with brown nodes. The leaves are linear lanceolate; length 1¼ in (3 cm); width ⅕ in (5 mm). The leaf blade is pale green and glossy on the upper surface. White flowers, 5–6 in short spikes, ⅗ in (1.5 cm) in length, appear in summer.

H.subalpina is to be preferred for the garden with its crowded flower spikes. Zone 7.

H.'Gannymede'

This cultivar is named after the youth who took Hebe's place, when she was in disgrace, as cup bearer to the senior Gods. This plant was originally labelled H.speciosa, but was found to be a hybrid from it. After much searching for its name and origin, it was decided to name it as it was worth growing.

Makes a rounded much branched shrub growing to about 54 in (135 cm). The stems are light brown, with darker brown nodes. The leaves are slightly bronzy green, lanceolate and oblanceolate; length 2–4 in (5–10 cm); width ¾–1⅖ in (2–3.5 cm) wide. The leaf edge and young leaf bud are plum colour. Purple flowers, fading lighter, are crowded on spikes 3 in (7.5 cm) long narrowing to the tip, in mid to late summer.

Where half hardy shrubs can be grown, it is worth finding a place in the border for this summer flowering shrub. Zone 10.

H.'Gauntlettii'

See H.'Eveline' for description. H.'Gloriosa' has been described as synonymous with H.'Gauntlettii', but this is not the case, as it grows to twice the height.

H.gibbsii

Grows only in the Dun Mountain Range, Nelson Province, South Island, NZ at 3,000–4,000 ft (914–1,220 m) and was first found by Mr F.G. Gibbs on Mt. Rintoul and Ben Nevis, NZ. This species is named after him, in recognition of the plant discoveries he made in the area. Frederick Gibbs (1866–1953) was a schoolmaster born in England. H.gibbsii is found growing amongst rocks.

A sparingly branched shrub about 12 in (30 cm) in height. The branchlets are ringed with scars of fallen leaves. This is a distinctive species because of the down turned hairs along the margins of the elliptic to ovate leaf blades, usually red edged, which are thick and glaucous green; length ½–¾ in (1.25–2 cm); width ¼–½ in (6–12.5 mm). White flowers, closely placed at the ends of the shoots, appear in late May or June.

A hardy rock plant. Zone 7.

H.glaucophylla

The name means blue grey and refers to the foliage of this plant, which grows on the shrubby banks and gullies in the tussock grassland from South Marlborough to mid Canterbury, South Island, NZ.

Well branched, fairly erect with rounded outline, growing up to 48 in (120 cm) in height. The branchlets are slender, brown in colour and age grey. The leaves are very small, ½ in (1.25 cm) in length, older leaves can grow to ¾ in (2 cm); width ³⁄₁₆ in (4 mm). The leaf blade is greeny grey, glabrous, lanceolate, narrowing to the tip and spreading. Lilac flowers in short racemes, 1⅖ in (3.5 cm) long, appear in leaf axils near the ends of the branchlets, in summer.

A plant for the shrub border. Zone 7.

(This description also applies to H.'Darwiniana' (IS) which differs in growing slightly taller, not being so compact and leaves are slightly concave and sometimes sickle shaped.)

H.glaucophylla 'Variegata'

A variegated leaved shrub growing up to 42 in (105 cm) in height. A

PLATE 1
The Whipcord Hebes

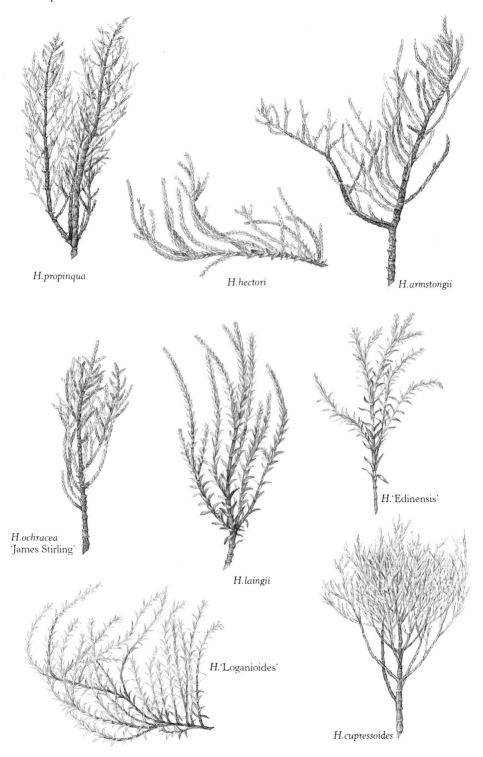

H.propinqua

H.hectori

H.armstongii

H.ochracea
'James Stirling'

H.laingii

H.'Edinensis'

H.'Loganioides'

H.cupressoides

PLATE 2
The Bronze Foliaged Hebes

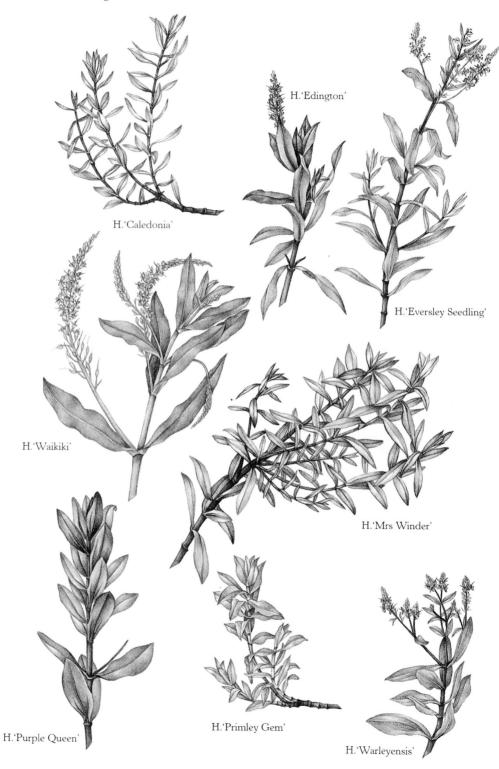

H.'Caledonia'

H.'Edington'

H.'Eversley Seedling'

H.'Waikiki'

H.'Mrs Winder'

H.'Purple Queen'

H.'Primley Gem'

H.'Warleyensis'

PLATE 3
The Border Hebes

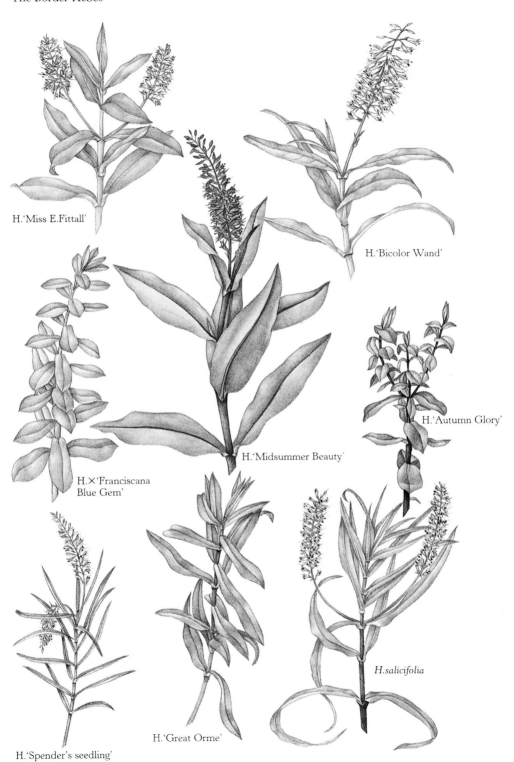

H.'Miss E.Fittall'

H.'Bicolor Wand'

H.×'Franciscana
Blue Gem'

H.'Midsummer Beauty'

H.'Autumn Glory'

H.salicifolia

H.'Great Orme'

H.'Spender's seedling'

PLATE 4
Low Growing and Ground Covering Hebes and Parahebes

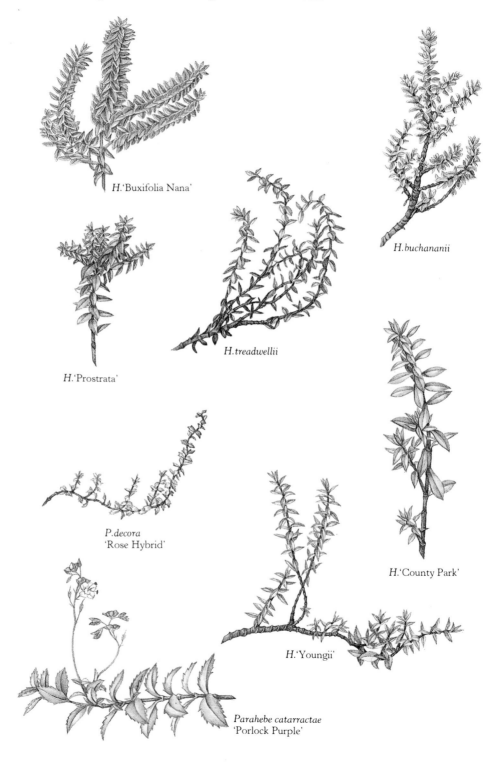

H.'Buxifolia Nana'

H.buchananii

H.'Prostrata'

H.treadwellii

H.'County Park'

P.decora
'Rose Hybrid'

H.'Youngii'

Parahebe catarractae
'Porlock Purple'

PLATE 5
The Outstanding Hebes

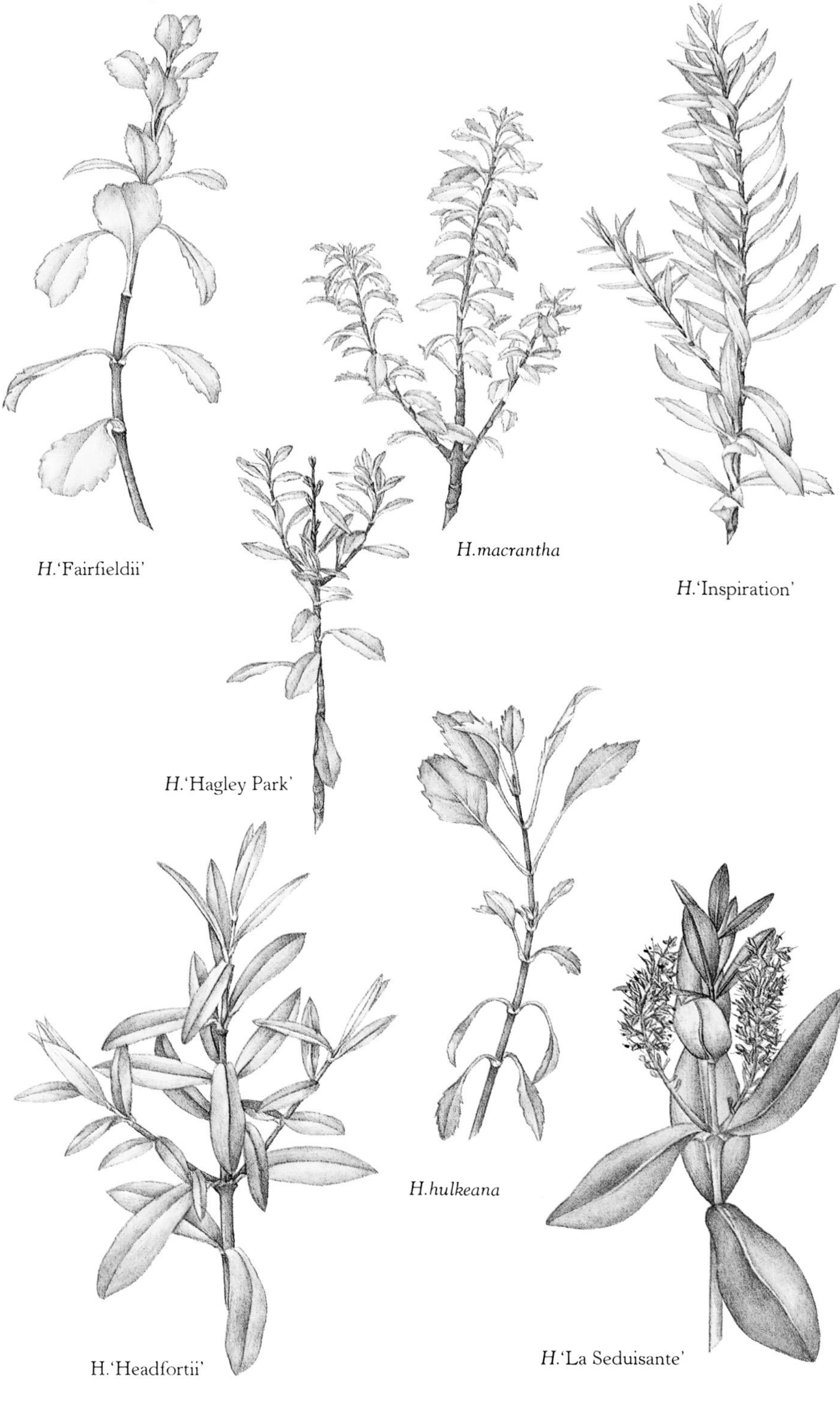

H.'Fairfieldii'

H.macrantha

H.'Inspiration'

H.'Hagley Park'

H.hulkeana

H.'Headfortii'

H.'La Seduisante'

PLATE 6
The Grey Foliaged Hebes

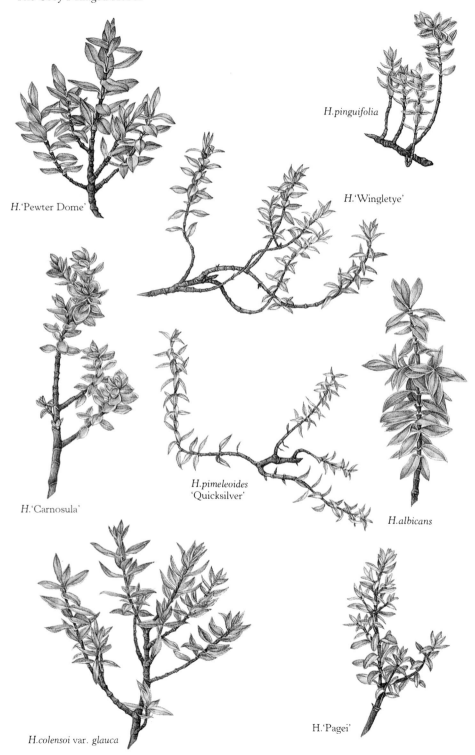

H.'Pewter Dome'

H.pinguifolia

H.'Wingletye'

H.'Carnosula'

H.pimeleoides
'Quicksilver'

H.albicans

H.colensoi var. *glauca*

H.'Pagei'

PLATE 7
The Variegated Hebes

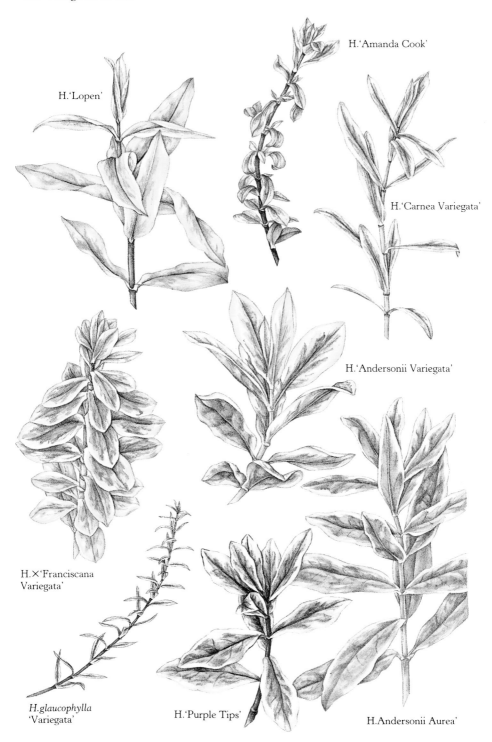

H.'Amanda Cook'

H.'Lopen'

H.'Carnea Variegata'

H.'Andersonii Variegata'

H.×'Franciscana
Variegata'

H.glaucophylla
'Variegata'

H.'Purple Tips'

H.Andersonii Aurea'

PLATE 8
The Green and Yellow Foliaged Hebes

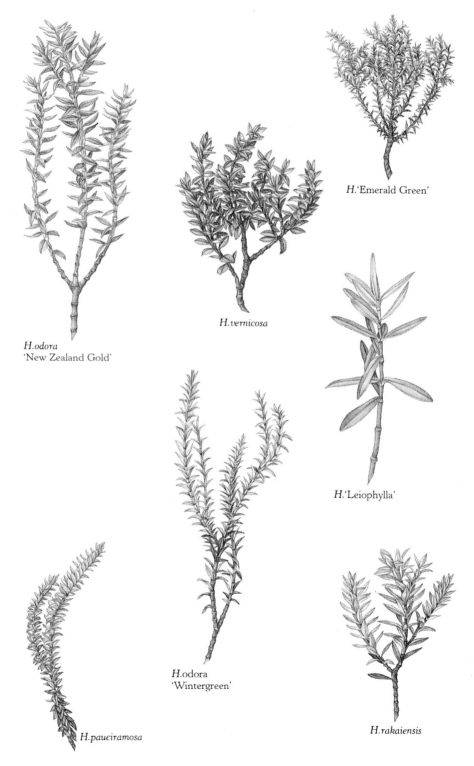

H.'Emerald Green'

H.vernicosa

H.odora
'New Zealand Gold'

H.'Leiophylla'

H.odora
'Wintergreen'

H.paueiramosa

H.rakaiensis

compact and rounded shrub, the stems are lighter brown with darker brown nodes, ageing brown. The leaves are grey green edged with cream, otherwise like *H.glaucophylla* in size and shape, and which see for fuller details of leaves, flowers and hardiness.

H.glaucophylla 'Variegata' prefers sun and some protection and could be not quite so hardy. A worthwhile shrub to grow in the garden. Zone 8, or Zone 9 in some areas.

H.'Glengarriff'

Little known about the origin of this cultivar which is low growing, with upright branches, to about 9 in (22.5 cm). The branchlets are greeny brown, the nodes brown ageing to a grey brown with the brown nodal rings still showing. The leaves are green with a coating of fine grey hairs, upward growing at first then spreading, with the central vein raised on the upper surface; length ½ in (1.25 cm); width ³/₁₀ in (8 mm). The leaf blade is oval, slightly concave with margins free of hairs. Short spikes of white flowers are carried towards the ends of the stems, in summer.

A plant for the rock garden. Zone 7.

H.'Gloriosa'

It had been said that *H.*'Gauntlettii' and *H.*'Gloriosa' were synonymous, until autumn 1975, when *H.*'Gloriosa' was found growing strongly in a

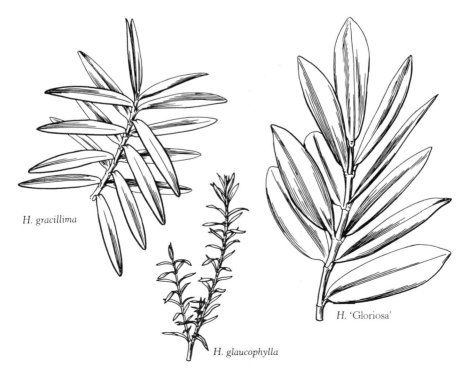

H. gracillima

H. glaucophylla

H. 'Gloriosa'

8.7 H. gracillima, H.glaucophylla, H.'*Gloriosa*'

Guernsey garden. Although the flowers may be similar in colour, the flowering time is July in *H.*'Gloriosa' and mid August onward with *H.*'Gauntlettii', but the main difference is in height. *H.*'Gauntlettii grows to 54 in (135 cm); *H.*'Gloriosa' grows to twice that height, namely 108 in (270 cm). When not in flower, leaf length can be helpful; 2½ (6.5 cm) in *H.*'Gauntlettii' and 3 in (7.5 cm) with *H.*'Gloriosa'. *H.*'Pink Pearl' is given as another name for *H.*'Gloriosa', but as yet this cultivar has not been found.

Makes a shapely, tall shrub in coastal districts or where it can be grown. The branchlets are greeny brown with a darker ring where the leaves join. The leaves are elliptic or elliptic lanceolate, upward growing then spreading. The leaf blade is green, with the under surface paler with a plum coloured midrib; length up to 3 in (7.5 cm); width ³/₄–1 in (2–2.5 cm). The leaf bud is often covered by plumb coloured leaves. Deep purple pink flowers are carried on 5–6 in (12.5–15 cm) spikes, in July.

A fine shrub for the larger sheltered garden, especially near the coast. Zone 10.

H.'Gnome'

A small decumbent cultivar, which arose at County Park Nursery, Essex a seedling with *H.*'Youngii' (*H.*'Carl Teschner') as one parent. In appearance a little like *H.*'Edinensis'.

Grows to about 6 in (15 cm) and is spreading. The stems are lighter green and glossy. The leaves are very small, no more than ¼ in (6 mm) in length, and very little less in width; the leaf blade is green, shiny and ovate. The leaves are four ranked, clasping the stem at the base, then grow outward and upward. Small violet flowers are carried near the ends of the branchlets, in summer.

A plant for the rock garden or trough. Zone 8.

H.'Godefroyana'

This is a clone or hybrid from *H.pinguifolia* raised in the garden of Monsieur Godefroy Lebeuf at Argenteuil in France from seed from an unknown source around 1876. Carrière described the plant in 1888 to which he gave the name *Veronica godefroyana*. It is still a rare plant.

Rather loose growing up to about 12 in (30 cm), eventually forming a rounded bush. The branches grow upright at first, then spread with their own weight. The branchlets are brown and lustrous with dark nodal rings. The leaves are grey green, about ½ in (1.25 cm) long and ¼ in (6 mm) wide, less grey and less glaucous than the parent. The leaf blade is ovate or ovate oblong. The flower spikes are well filled with white flowers in summer arising near the ends of the stems.

An interesting rock garden shrub. Zone 7.

H.gracillima

(Latin — gracillima = very slender, refers to the branches) Found in damp and swampy places.

Fairly upright growing, with branches not compactly arranged. The branchlets are yellow green at first becoming gradually browner with age; the nodes are grey brown. Grows to a height of 48 in (120 cm), sometimes more such as where it is found on the west coast of South Island, NZ around Westport. The leaves are narrow lanceolate to oblong; length 1½ in (4 cm); width ¼ in (6 mm). The leaf blade is glabrous, bright green above, duller below, upright growing at first then spreading, tending to be a little fleshy. There are racemes of 4–14 white flowers, in summer.

Needs maybe some protection in exposed sites. A pleasant foil for the early flowering shrubs. Zone 8.

H.'Gran's Favourite'

A seedling from H.'Midsummer Beauty' growing to 36 in (90 cm) in height.

A long flowering, compact, rounded shrub. The leaves are lanceolate, 2½ in (6.5 cm) long and ½ in (1.25 cm) wide. The leaf blades are mauve on the under surface around and close to the leaf bud. Spikes of pale mauve flowers, 3–4 in (7.5–10 cm) long, have reddish purple stamens and anthers. Summer and autumn flowering.

If flower is wanted, then this shrub raised at County Park Nursery in Essex should be considered. Zone 9.

H.'Great Orme'

A hybrid from H.'Carnea' forming a much branched, rounded shrub growing to a height of 54 in (135 cm) or more, and up to 48 in (120 cm) in width. The stems are light brown. The leaves are oblong lanceolate up to 2¾ in (6 cm) in length, and ½ in (1.25 cm) wide. The leaf blade is shiny yellow green, growing upright at first, then spreading and down turning. Bright pink flowers on upward growing spikes, 2–4 in (5–10 cm) long, appear from late summer into autumn near the ends of the branchlets. The flowers fade white to give a two colour effect.

A lovely cultivar for the sheltered garden away from severe frosts and penetrating winds. Zone 9.

H.'Greensleeves'

A seedling from H.ochracea, erect, bushy and growing to about 24 in (60 cm). A semi-whipcord cultivar that differs from the parent, as the leaves are stiff, green and tending to out turn at the tips. The branchlets are covered in fine hairs and are greeny brown in colour. Up to 12 sessile flowers, white in colour, are carried in a terminal spike about 1¾ in (4.5 cm) long, during May and June.

A useful foliage plant and an alternative to a conifer. Introduced by County Park Nursery of Essex. Zone 7.

H.haastii

A low, woody shrub named after Julius von Haast (1822–1887) who was born in Germany and came to New Zealand as a geologist and explorer.

This species is found high up on mountains at 6,000–7,000 ft (1,830–2,134 m) from Nelson to Otago, as well as on Mt. Cook, South Island, NZ.

This is a sprawling plant with crooked stems, that are crowded with small, overlapping leaves, growing to 12 in (30 cm). The branchlets are light green in colour. The leaves are rounded or ovate, ¼–½ in (6–12.5 mm) long and up to ¼ in (6 mm) wide. The leaf blade is slightly concave, fleshy, green and shiny; the margin is lighter green. Small, white flowers in an ovoid head or spike, up to 1½ in (4 cm) long, appear at the ends of the stems, in summer.

This is a difficult species to grow, so a challenge for the alpine enthusiast. It needs shaded, well drained soil. Zone 7.

H.haastii var. *macrocalyx* and var. *humilis*

Mention might be made of two varieties: first, var. *macrocalyx* from Canterbury Mts Waimakariri Valley to Otira, South Island, NZ, which has obovate to spathulate leaves about ½ in (1.25 cm) by ¼ in (6 mm) wide; secondly, *H.haastii* var. *humilis* from the slopes of Mt. French near Hector's Col, South Island, NZ, which has leaves that are more elliptic, narrowing at the lower end to a winged stalk or petiole. The leaf also narrows towards the tip and is often keeled. Other details and hardiness similar to the parent *H.haastii*.

H.'Hagley Park'

(syn. *H.*'Hagleyensis') A chance seedling that occurred in the alpine garden of Hagley Park, Christchurch, South Island, NZ and was discovered, raised and named by W.B. Brockie. Further controlled hybridisation has shown that the parents were *H.hulkeana* and *H.raoulii*, which was the female parent.

An erect to slightly spreading shrub with the branchlets covered in fine down pointing hairs. Grows to a height of about 16 in (40 cm). The leaf blade is obovate to oblong elliptic, lightly crenate or bluntly toothed and glabrous. The petiole is up to ¼ in (6 mm) in length and slightly winged. The leaf margins are reddish, the leaves are spreading. Rosy purple flowers are carried in terminal panicles, 4½ in (11.5 cm) in length, in early summer. Longer panicles do occur, even up to 11 in (28 cm) in length.

An attractive, free flowering cultivar for the rock garden or the border. At its best in sunny positions. Zone 9.

H.'Hartii'

A prostrate, slender shrub with spreading habit with its leaves displayed in one plane, so making it a useful cultivar for trailing over rocks or rock walls. *H.diosmifolia* could be one parent, but other parent is not known. Cultivar is named after Mr L.B. Hart of Lawrence, Otago, South Island, NZ.

Growing to a height of 4 in (10 cm), the branchlets are green to slightly purplish. The leaves are oblanceolate, ½–⅝ in (1.25–1.5 cm) long by ¼ in (6 mm) wide. The leaf blade is green, shiny and duller beneath. Racemes of mauve flowers, fading to white, 2 in (5 cm) long, appear in late spring or early summer. A rock garden plant. Zone 9.

H.'Headfortii'

A half hardy shrub raised at Headfort, Eire from seeds sent from New Zealand. Same or similar parentage to H.'Inspiration'; sometimes found with the name H.'BlueBoy'.

A rounded, well branched, compact growing shrub, which can reach 48 in (120 cm) in height. The branchlets are bronzy green, slightly deeper at the nodes. The leaves are dark bronzy green crowded on the branches and tending to turn slightly in one plane. The leaves increase slightly in size from the top downwards. The leaf blade is obovate oblong and paler below; length $\frac{1}{2}$–1$\frac{1}{2}$ in (1.25–4 cm); width $\frac{4}{10}$–$\frac{1}{2}$ in (1–1.25 cm). (The first measurement is from the leaves at the top of the stem and the second from the lower leaves.) The bronze flower buds compliment the bright purplish blue flowers that follow. The axillary flower stalk usually branches into three at a point about 1 in (2.5 cm) from the base. Each spike is also about 1 in (2.5 cm) long and displayed on a pedicel $\frac{1}{2}$ in (1.25 cm) in length. The spikes are $\frac{3}{5}$ in (1.6 cm) wide, narrowing to the tip. This arrangement means that the flowers are displayed clear of the leaves, in early summer.

A tender Hebe, but a useful shrub for the flower arranger. Worth considering growing in a tub outside in the summer and bringing under cover in the winter, when frosts and cold winds only allow the growing of hardy shrubs. Zone 10.

H.hectori

A whipcord whose natural habitat is the sub alpine scrub in the mountains of South Canterbury and Otago as well as Mt. Alta and abundantly in Fiordland, South Island, NZ. Named after Sir James Hector (1834–1907), a Scot who came to New Zealand as a geologist and explorer and who helped to found the Wellington Botanic Gardens.

A stoutly branched, rather erect and rigid shrub, growing up to 30 in (75 cm). The branchlets are yellow green, ageing to browny yellow and becoming ringed with old leaf scars. The yellow brown leaves are very small, $\frac{1}{8}$ in (3 mm) in length, overlapping and joined at the base for half their length. They are ovate, are rounded underneath and turn in towards the stem. Spikes, up to $\frac{1}{2}$ in (1.25 cm) in length, carrying about 15 small, white flowers, can be found in the axils of the leaves at the end of the branchlets, in summer.

The unique colour of the stems make this shrub a useful plant for the border or rock garden. Zone 7.

H.hectori var. demissa

A low and spreading variety of H.hectori growing up to 6 in (15 cm) and found in moist grassy banks near streams in the Rock and Pillar Range, South Island, NZ. A useful ground covering shrub for the garden. Zone 7.

H.'Hidcote'

As the name implies, a hybrid from the famous Cotswold Garden, England. Not unlike H.'Violet Wand' in leaf and habit, with any variations only very slight. Flower colour too is the same, so see H.'Violet Wand' for a full description.

H.'Hielan Lassie'

A smaller leaved H.speciosa hybrid; H.'Helse' is synonymous. Origin is unknown.

A fairly compact growing cultivar with both flowers and foliage for interest. Shrub height is 54 in (135 cm), fairly wide spread to give a rounded bush. The stems are reddish brown, ageing more brown. Both elliptic and obovate leaves appear on same bush, up to 1½ in (4 cm) in length and ½ in (1.25 cm) wide. The under surfaces are duller with the buds, midribs and under surfaces of young leaves reddish purple. The leaves are close together on the stems and spreading. Violet flowers, in spikes 2½ in (6.5 cm) long and ½ in (1.25 cm) wide, appear near the ends of the branchlets. The 1 in (2.5 cm) stalks help to display the crowded flowers more attractively in summer. Zone 10 or sheltered areas Zone 9.

H.'Highdownensis'

Named after the garden of Sir Frederick Stearn of Highdown, West Sussex.

An erect growing shrub, rather like H.'Great Orme' in growth, but only growing to 54 in (135 cm) in height. Brown stemmed with darker nodal rings, where the leaves join the stem. The leaves are narrow, elliptic oblong up to 2 in (5 cm) in length and ⁴⁄₁₀ in (1 cm) in width. The leaf blade is light to mid green, shiny, but paler beneath. Purple, almost royal blue, flowers appear on narrow spikes, the same length as the leaves, in summer.

A useful and interesting addition to the shrub border in the protected, warmer gardens. Zone 10.

H.'Highdown Pink'

A robust growing hybrid, with H.speciosa as one parent, from the garden of Sir Frederick Stearn in West Sussex.

A much branched, upright growing, yet rounded shrub, with green and finely pubescent branchlets growing to a height of 60 in (150 cm). The leaves are elliptic, narrowly ovate, glossy green, but paler beneath, up to 2½ in (6.5 cm) long and ½ in (1.25 cm) wide. The leaf blade is fairly stiff and glaucous in appearance; the margins of the leaves turn downwards. The leaf bud has a rounded sinus. Bright rose pink flowers, with darker pink bases to the petals, appear in summer. The crowded flowers are carried in cylindrical spikes 2 in (5 cm) or more in length, 1 in (2.5 cm) in width, held on pedicels nearly 1 in (2.5 cm) in length.

A half hardy free flowering shrub for the border in the sheltered garden. Zone 10.

H.'Highdown Pink'

H.'Highdownensis'

8.8 H. *'Highdown Pink'*, H. *'Highdownensis'*

H.hulkeana

Found on banks and rocky bluffs from sea level to 3,000 ft (915 m) in Marlborough and North Canterbury, South Island, NZ. It has been named after Mr T.H. Hulke and is accepted as one of the best species of Hebe and is known as the New Zealand Lilac. It grows better in dry districts. Where the humidity is high, then it is liable to be attacked by the disease downy mildew (*Peronospera grisea*).

An erect, rather loosely branched and spreading shrub, growing to a height of 24 in (60 cm). The slender branchlets are purplish red in colour and finely pubescent. The leaves are oblong elliptic to sub orbicular, narrowing towards the stalk or petiole. The leaf margins are toothed and reddish in colour. The leaf blade is dark green and glossy and the underneath paler; length 1½ in (4 cm); width ¾ in (2 cm) with a stalk ½ in (1.25 cm) long. Lavender flowers are carried on a broad, branched, terminal panicle 6–9 in (15–22.5 cm) long including a stalk which can be up to 4 in (10 cm) in length. The branches of the panicle can be up to 3 in (7.5 cm) in length. Flowers early summer.

Be selective in your choice of plant, there are some poorer forms about, and in finding the right position, which should be warm, sunny and dry, with a well drained soil. Zone 9 (10).

H.'Hybrid Purple'

A *H.speciosa* hybrid raised in Cannington near Bridgwater in Somerset.

A much branched, fairly compact, rounded shrub, growing to a height of 54–60 in (135–150 cm). The branchlets are purplish red but ageing brown. The mid green leaves are paler beneath with a purplish red midrib. The young leaves and leaf bud are also purplish red, but become greener later. The leaf blade is elliptic to ovate, upward growing then spreading, up to 2 in (5 cm) in length and almost 1 in (2.5 cm) in width. Bright purple flowers crowd the 2–3 in (5–7.5 cm) spikes in summer, making this an attractive neat shrub for the warmer, sheltered garden. Zone 10.

H.imbricata

(Latin — imbricatus = overlap, as in overlapping tiles) The name refers to the very small leaves which are closely pressed to the stems of this small whipcord shrub, which is to be found on Mt. Cleughearn in Fiordland, South Island. NZ.

An erect, much branched, rounded shrub, 18–24 in (45–60 cm) in height. The branchlets are rather rigid and glossy. The leaves are $1/16$ in (1.5 mm) in length, attached at the base for one-third of their length, ovate and closely pressed to the stems, green to yellow green in colour. White flowers are sparsely produced at the ends of the branchlets.

An alpine shrub, unlikely to be in cultivation outside New Zealand, or within it. Zone 7.

H.'Inspiration'

A hybrid between H.speciosa and H.diosmifolia originating in New Zealand and introduced by Messrs Duncan and Davies of New Plymouth, NZ in the 1950s, and well suited to growing in coastal regions.

A rather spreading shrub, which can grow up to 48 in (120 cm). The stems are purplish brown and slightly pubescent. The leaves are dark green, the leaf blade oblanceolate and oblong elliptic (being a H.speciosa cross), 1 in (2.5 cm) in length by $3/10$ in (8 mm) wide and slightly hairy. Purple flowers crowd the branches in summer and are carried in racemes $1\frac{1}{2}$ in (4 cm) or more long and up to 1 in (2.5 cm) wide at the ends of the branchlets. The racemes are carried on short stalks and may be branched.

A shrub for the coastal districts and especially a warm sheltered garden where it grows compactly with its leaves tending to turn to one plane. Zone 10.

H.insularis

(Latin — insula = from an island) This shrubby species is found on ledges on sea cliffs on Great Island and South West Island of Three Kings Islands, off the northern tip (nearest equator) of North island, NZ.

An erect to spreading shrub with hairy stems, growing to a height of about 24 in (60 cm). The leaves are green, spreading, glaucous, if not glabrous. The leaf blade is up to 1 in (2.5 cm) long and $2/5$ in (1 cm) wide, elliptic to oblong. The leaf bud has a small, narrow sinus. The pale blue flowers are carried on laterals $1\frac{3}{4}$ in (4.5 cm) long, often in threes and forming a corymbose head at the end of the branchlet, in early summer.

Certainly a half hardy species, so a frost free, coastal site is needed for this shrub. Zone 10.

H.'James Platt'

A hybrid rather like H.'Colwall' only a little more spreading and named after a plantsman, James Platt. Growing to a height of 24 in (60 cm), the branchlets are brown with a hint of reddish purple. The leaves are green and spreading; the leaf blade elliptic, rounded up to ½ in (1.25 cm) long and ¼ in (6 mm) wide, concave with a red edge. Purple flowers in short racemes, about 1 in (2.5 cm) long, appear at the end of the branchlets in early summer. The racemes are sometimes terminal.

Zone 9; but can be damaged in severe winters.

H.'Jane Holden'

A large leaved hybrid collected in Devon and about which little is known.

Erect, well branched, rounded in outline growing to a height of 48 in (120 cm). The branchlets are yellow green to green. The leaves are green, shiny, paler below with prominent midrib. The leaf blade is elliptic; length 3 in (7.5 cm); width 1 in (2.5 cm). The midrib is depressed and lighter on the upper surface. The leaves are erect at first then spreading. Pinky purple flowers are carried on a spike about the same length as the leaves. Summer flowering.

Could be Zone 9, so should be a useful shrub to grow.

H.'Jewel'

Possibly a *H.salicifolia* cross or a cross with a hybrid from *H.salicifolia*, which makes a rounded, dense bush.

Much branched, fairly erect and looking rather stiff; height 54 in (135 cm). The stems are green with a slight pubescence. The leaves are oblong elliptic, 2–2½ in (5–6.5 cm) in length and 7/10 in (1.7 cm) wide. The leaf blade is green, slightly shiny, paler below. The leaves are close together on the stems, upward growing. The leaf bud has a small, oval sinus. Blue flowers are carried in fairly crowded spikes, 2 in (5 cm) long with 1½ in (4 cm) stalks. The spikes are at an angle to the stem, with the flowers tending to depress or spread that end of the spike. July flowering, near the ends of the branches.

A good background shrub but rather short flowering time. Zone 9; and possibly Zone 8 in more protected sites.

H.'Johny Day'

A seedling that arose at County Park Nursery in Essex from *H.*'La Seduisante Purple Tips' (known also as *H.speciosa* 'Tricolor', and as *H.*'Purple Tips', which see). A newer cultivar growing to a height of 48 in (120 cm) or more in warmer gardens. It has violet purple flowers (given as magenta in some descriptions) and purple foliage. See *H.*'La Seduisante' for more details.

It could be a good shrub for foliage. Half hardy. Zone 10.

H.'Joyce Parker'

A wide spreading, fast growing, ground covering shrub, from County Park Nursery in Essex, growing to about 15 in (37–40 cm) in height. It has green stems and pale green leaves, which tend to lie back along the branches. The leaves are slightly obovate, 1 in (2.5 cm) in length and ⅖ in (1 cm) wide. Loose racemes of pale mauve flowers appear in summer.
Zone 9.

H.'Kewensis'

Named after the Royal Botanic Garden, Kew, Richmond, Surrey, but so far little more has been discovered about this compact growing shrub, which reaches a height of about 10 in (25 cm). The branchlets are greeny brown with darker brown nodes. The leaves are grey green, finely pubescent on both surfaces; length ¾ in (2 cm); width ⅕ in (5 mm). The margin is free of hairs and yellow green; the under surface paler. The leaves grow upwards, giving a spiky look to the plant. Short spikes of white flowers appear near the tips of the branchlets, in May. The spikes are a little longer than the leaves.

An interesting small shrub for the rock garden with its spiky looking, lanceolate, slightly concave leaves. Zone 7.

H.'Killiney'

Named after the town in Eire in which Watson's Nursery is situated and where this cultivar originated.

A compact, much branched, rounded shrub, with browny green stems, growing to a height of 54 in (135 cm). The leaves are lanceolate, narrowing at the tips, apple green in colour, paler below; length 2½ in (6.5–7 cm); width ⁷⁄₁₀ in (1.7 cm), with a slightly shiny surface. Steel blue flowers are carried in spikes about the same length as the leaves, near the ends of the branchlets, in summer. The pedicels carrying the spikes are 1¼ in (3 cm) long.

A reliable shrub, to provide background to a flower border or gap filler in the shrub bed, with its flowers and upward growing leaves giving a spiky appearance. Zone 9; or could be Zone 8 in sheltered gardens.

H.'Kirkii'

Named after the botanist, Thomas Kirk (1828–1898), this hybrid was found in Upper Rangitata, South Island, NZ. *H.salicifolia* is possibly one of the parents.

A rounded shrub, well branched and up to 48 in (120 cm) in height with green stems. The leaves are glossy green, of rather heavy or thick texture, ovate, up to 1¼ in (3 cm) in length and ⅖ in (1 cm) in width. There can be slight toothing along the margins. White flowers in slender spikes, 2–4 in (5–10 cm) long, appear in June.

Not widely cultivated, but could be a useful background shrub. Zone 7.

H.'La Favourite'

A hybrid of unknown origin and bearing a resemblance to H.'Alicia Amherst', both in flowers and foliage.

Upright growing, well branched with stout stems which are light green in colour; height 60 in (150 cm). The leaves are broadly ovate, appear rather leathery, upward growing then spreading later. The leaf blade is green, paler below, upper leaves 2½ in (6.5 cm) long, but lower leaves on the branches can reach 4 in (10 cm) in length; width 1–1½ in (2.5–4 cm). The leaves and stems are finely pubescent. Mauvy or royal purple flowers are carried in cylindrical spikes 2½ in (6.5 cm) in length and 1 in (2.5 cm) in diameter at the end of the branchlets. The spike stalk is ½ in (1.25 cm) long. Summer flowering.

A half hardy cultivar grown for its flowers in warmer sheltered gardens and as a background shrub. Zone 10.

H.laingii

Named after R.M. Laing (1865–1941), a botanist and teacher, this whip-cord like shrub is found in subalpine grass on Mt. Anglem, Stewart Island, NZ.

A smaller growing whipcord with branches that tend to grow outward at first then upward, to a height of 6–8 in (15–20 cm). Much branched, with green stems becoming brown. The leaves are very small, ovate, joined for half their length then outward growing; the younger leaves are adpressed. The leaf blade is thick, glossy green under pubescence, margins yellow green; length ⅕ in (5 mm); width ⅒ in (2.5 mm). Short spikes, eight-flowered, white, and about ⅖ in (1 cm) in length, appear in summer.

A useful whipcord for the smaller garden or trough or rock garden. Needs to be better known. Zone 7.

H.'La Reine des Blanches'

(Queen of the Whites) A hybrid, probably of French origin and from H.salicifolia as evidence by the slight toothing towards the tips of some leaves.

Strong growing, well branched, fairly neat and rounded in outline, to a height of 60 in (150 cm). The stems are green becoming greeny brown, like the nodes. The leaves are oblong lanceolate; length 3 in (7.5 cm); width ⁶⁄₁₀ in (1.5 cm). The leaf blade is mid to dark green with a lighter green midrib and leaf edge, spreading and down turning. The upper surface is shiny; underneath is duller. White flowers, larger than those of H.salicifolia, fairly widely spaced on spikes 3½ in (9 cm) long, nearly 1 in (2.5 cm) wide, appear near the ends of the branchlets in summer and again in autumn.

A pleasant background shrub with a longer flowering period. Zone 9; could be lower where sheltered from cold winds.

H.'La Seduisante'

The name in French means 'attractive' and this older *H.speciosa* hybrid is certainly attractive and popular.

Upright growing, much branched and with purplish brown stems, which are finely pubescent; height 54 in (135 cm). The bark can split in severe frosts. The leaves are broadly elliptic, dark green and shiny above, paler below with a purplish brown midrib. The leaves round the growing point are purplish brown on the under surface. The leaf blade is spreading; length 2¾–4 in (7 cm); width up to 1½ in (4.5 cm). The purplish margin to the leaf is more noticeable on the underside. Violet purple flowers are closely placed on spikes 3 in (7.5 cm) long or longer; the pedicels are 1 in (2.5 cm) long. The spikes are up to ⅘ in (2 cm) wide, appear in summer and can be up to 4 in (10 cm) long.

A half hardy cultivar well worth trying to grow in the warmer coastal garden or elsewhere. Zone 9 (10).

H.lavaudiana

Named in honour of C.F. Lavaud (1798–1878), Captain of the French ship *L'Aube*. This shrub is found in rocky places on the French settled Banks Peninsula, on the east coast of South Island, NZ.

Low growing, up to 12 in (30 cm), the branches are spreading at first then upward growing and rather sparse. The leaves are yellowy green, thick and leathery, the margins red in colour and broadly toothed. The leaf blade is broadly obovate to rounded (egg shaped), up to 1 in (2.5 cm) in width and about the same in length. Rosy pink buds opening to white flowers, are carried in terminal panicles up to 2 in (5 cm) across, in May.

Half hardy and for the warmer garden, maybe along the coast. Too close, humid a condition can encourage downy mildew (*Peronospera grisea*). Zone 10.

H.'Leiophylla' (IS)

(Greek — leios = smooth and phylla, a leaf) A smooth leaved shrub from the Nelson Region and across to Otago, South island, NZ and from sea level to 3,000 ft (915 m). Until the medium leaved Hebes from the Nelson Region are sorted out, *H.*'Leiophylla' remains an uncertain species (IS). It is found in open country or on the edge of bush.

A neat, much branched shrub, rounded and spreading, upright growing to a height of 12 ft (3.65 m) in the wild, but in Britain it may reach 54–60 in (135–150 cm). The leaves are glabrous, light to mid green, narrowly oblong or oblong elliptic, ¾–1¼ in (2–3 cm) in length and ⅕ in (5 mm) wide, turning slightly to one plane on the greeny brown stem, on which the leaves are closely arranged. Slender spikes of white flowers up to 4½ in (11.5 cm) long, ¾ in (2 cm) wide, appear near the ends of the branchlets. Flowering time is mid July.

In flower this is a very attractive Hebe, but needs to get established. Zone 8; but this is questionable in exposed gardens or positions in the northern half of Britain.

H.'Lewisii'

A much travelled cultivar, since it was discovered growing wild on the downs above Timaru, South Island, NZ by J.B. Armstrong in 1881. It was named after Mr Lewis, a nurseryman in Timaru at that time. H.'Lewisii' arrived in Tresco in the Isles of Scilly in 1894 and in Guernsey around the same time. It is still growing in these islands today. A hybrid between H.elliptica and H.salicifolia, which has been proved.

An erect but branching shrub growing to more than 60 in (150 cm) in height. The branchlets are stout, brown in colour with darker brown nodes and finely hairy. The leaves are bright glossy green, slightly wavy, spreading, up to 2½ in (6.5 cm) in length and ¾–1 in (2–2.5 cm) wide. Some of the lower leaves on the branches can grow up to 4 in (10 cm) long and 1½ in (4 cm) wide. The leaf blade is elliptic oblong narrowing to the base. Violet flowers, but white below the lobes, are crowded into spikes 1½–2½ in (4–6.5 cm) in length, near the tips of the branches in summer and at other times into autumn or even winter.

A very good coastal shrub to provide protection to less hardy Hebes, but worth growing for its flowers. Zone 9.

H.ligustrifolia

(Latin — ligustrum = privet, folia = leaves; so we have privet like foliage or leaves) A shrub from the open scrub and forest margins along the Bay of Islands, North Island, NZ.

A loosely branched shrub growing to about 36 in (90 cm). The stems are greyish brown and hairy. The leaves are light yellowish green, and vary over the bush from narrow lanceolate to ovate oblong. The leaves are spreading ¾–2 in (2–5 cm) in length and ⅕–½ in (5–13 mm) in width.

H.'Lindsayii'

H.'Lewisii'

8.9 H.'Lindsayii', H.'Lewisii'

White flowers are openly arranged at the ends of the branches in spikes, up to twice the length of the leaves, in early summer.

This Hebe is half hardy, but it has possibly not found its way to Britain yet. Zone 10.

H.'Lindsayii'

Raised and named by Robert Lindsay (1846–1913) when Curator of the Edinburgh Botanic Garden in Scotland.

An upright shrub, rounded in outline growing to about 30 in (75 cm), with purplish brown stems. The leaves are rounded, obovate, slightly concave and shiny, mid green in colour, about 1 in (2.5 cm) in length and ½ in (1.25 cm) in width. Pale pink flowers crowd the short spikes, about the same length as the leaves, at the ends of the branchlets, in summer.

A cultivar with interesting foliage, it has been found under other names such as H.'May Queen' and H.'Appleblossom'. May not stand severe weather. Zone 9.

H.'Loganioides'

The names means like a Logania, in this case *Logania depressa*, a native New Zealand shrub. The name Logania is in honour of James Logan (1674–1751), the Irish writer on botany. Parentage of this natural hybrid is unknown.

A heath like whipcord hybrid with yellow green, hairy stems, growing to a height of 10 in (25 cm). The bright green leaves are pressed against the stems for half their length, then spreading. The leaves are very small; length ⅕ in (5 mm); width ¹⁄₁₀ in (2 mm). The leaf blade is elliptic and finely hairy. White flowers clustered terminally or in the axils of the upper leaves of the branchlets, in June.

A worthwhile whipcord Hebe to grow in the rock garden, trough or front of the border. Zone 7.

H.'Long Acre'

The origin is unknown, but the east coast of Ireland has been suggested, as it is in some ways like H.'Autumn Glory', which could be one of its parents.

An erect growing shrub, more compact than H.'Autumn Glory', to a height of 36 in (90 cm). The branchlets are brown with darker brown nodes. The leaves are rounded, obovate or elliptical, spreading with a tendency to be convex; length 1¼ in (3 cm); width ½ in (1.25 cm) at widest part. The leaf blade is green with a lighter margin and younger leaves are shiny. The leaves can be slightly reddish on the lower surface. The clerical or reddish purple flowers, in short spikes 1¾ in (4.5 cm) in length, are carried in summer near the ends of the branchlets.

Not as hardy as H.'Autumn Glory', so needs a warmer garden to give its best display. Zone 9.

H.'Lopen'

A variegated branch was noticed on the shrub H.'Midsummer Beauty' growing in the garden of the Malt House, Hinton St George, Somerset, the home of the late Miss Lowe, by Mr E.J.G. Goddard, a nurseryman from Lopen Head in Somerset. Cuttings were taken and the variegated shrub was grown and named after the village. Grows to under 54 in (135 cm) in height, with leaves irregularly marked with streaks and patches of grey green, yellow and cream.

See H.'Midsummer Beauty' for rest of description. Zone 9, or even Zone 10.

H.lycopodioides

In Latin, the name means like a Lycopodium or Club Moss and refers to the growth habit of this whipcord Hebe, which is found in subalpine scrub and tussock grassland east of the Main Divide in Marlborough and Canterbury Regions in the mountains from 2,500–5,500 ft (660–1,676 m).

Fairly erect, much branched, rather rigid, with distinct four-angled branchlets, which are yellowish green. Grows to a height of about 24 in (60 cm). The leaves are tight pressed against the stems and joined at the base for one-third the length. The small, delta shaped leaves are only $\frac{1}{10}$ in (2 mm) in length, rounded, thick and appear striped through the yellow margins turning into blunt, green tips. Terminal racemes of 3–12 white flowers are carried in summer.

An ideal plant for a sunny rock garden or border, where the sun brings out the colour in the foliage. Zone 7.

H.'MacEwanii'

Of British origin with H.pimeleoides as one of the parents. Who MacEwan was is not known.

A rather erect shrub with dark purple branchlets, growing to a height of 15 in (37 cm). The leaves are ascending at first but spreading later, glaucous on both surfaces and up to $\frac{3}{5}$ in (1.5 cm) long and $\frac{1}{5}$ in (5 mm) wide; leaf blade is oblong lanceolate.

Mauve or mauvy blue flowers are carried on a branched raceme near the end of the branchlet, in early summer. The raceme is $2\frac{1}{2}$ in (6.5 cm) long; the branch spikes are $1–1\frac{1}{2}$ in (2.5–4 cm) long.

A shrub for the rock garden or front of border. Zone 8.

H.macrantha

One of the easily recognised Hebes from the Canterbury Alps and Central Southern Alps, South Island, NZ, where it is found in short alpine scrub at 2,500–5,000 ft (660–1,525 m).

A rather straggling, woody and sparsely branched shrub, growing to 18 in (45 cm) in height. The leaves are spreading, on short, erect petioles. The leaf blade is thick and rather leathery, pale to yellowish green in colour, $\frac{1}{2}–1$ in (1.25–2.5 cm) long and $\frac{1}{4}–\frac{1}{2}$ in (6–12.5 mm) wide. The leaf margin is bluntly and evenly toothed; the leaves are elliptic in shape.

95

As the name suggests, 2–6 large, closely placed, pure white flowers about 1 in (2.5 cm) across, appear at the ends of the branches, in spring.

The shrub is not as attractive as the flowers, but still worth growing. Hardy in New Zealand, but in Britain it can be lost in severe winters, hence Zone 9.

H.macrantha var. brachyphylla

(Latin — brachyphylla = opposite leaves, alternating at right angles) This variety differs in that it has broad elliptic to orbicular leaves and is found in the mountains of Marlborough and Nelson, South Island, NZ. Reddish leaf margins help to identify it.

H.macrocarpa

The name, in Latin, means having large fruits. Found around Hokianga and Mangonui and southwards in Auckland Province, North Island, NZ.

A variable, usually stiffly branched shrub, but can be straggly. Grows up to 5–6 ft (150–180 cm). The branchlets are browny green, glabrous and finely pubescent. The leaves are narrow elliptic to elliptic oblong, a little fleshy, spreading; length 3–5½ in (7.5–14 cm); width ½–1 in (1.25–2.5 cm). Colour dark green, paler beneath. The leaf bud is without a sinus.

Long spikes of white flowers, as long or longer than the leaves, appear in spring and summer.

A coastal shrub for the sheltered garden. Zone 10.

H.macrocarpa var. brevifolia

The name refers to the shorter flower spikes which are not quite as long as the leaves, otherwise the description is the same as for *H.macrocarpa* except that the flowers are reddish purple and the shrub grows only to about 36 in (90 cm). This variety comes from the vicinity of North Cape, North Island, NZ (sub tropical). Zone 10.

H.macrocarpa var. latisepala

The name, in Latin, means broad sepals which distinguishes this variety from *H.macrocarpa*. The other features that differ are the leaves are narrow oblong and it has bluish purple flowers in spikes shorter than the leaves, about 4 in (10 cm) long. Found on Great and Little Barrier Islands and from Whangarei Harbour to the north and the Coromandel Peninsula to the south, on the mainland of Auckland Province, North Island, NZ. See *H.macrocarpa* for details. Zone 10.

H.'Marjorie'

The origin is not known for this cultivar which is compact, much branched and growing as wide as it is tall.

A rounded shrub, it grows to 54 in (135 cm). The stems are green becoming brown later, with brown rings where the leaves join the stem. The leaves are elliptic narrowing towards the stem, up to 2 in (5 cm) in length and ½ in (1.25 cm) wide. The leaf blade is yellow green, shiny above and upward growing. Mauvy blue flowers fading to white give a bicolour effect. The fairly crowded spikes are the same length as the leaves and are carried on 1 in (2.5 cm) stalks.

A background shrub that is covered in flower for a short time in June and July. Zone 8.

H.matthewsii

This species has been named after Henry J. Matthews (1859–1909) and was collected by him in the Humboldt Mts, South Otago, South Island, NZ.

An erect, glabrous shrub with stout branchlets often purplish when young, growing up to 48 in (120 cm). The leaves tend to be fleshy, oblong or elliptic oblong, 1 in (2.5 cm) or more in length and about ½ in (1.25 cm) wide. The leaves on the young branchlets are often shorter and narrow. The flowers are fairly close together on tapering spikes up to 2½ in (6.5 cm) long at the top of the branchlets, white in colour, in mid-summer.

Mostly a border filling shrub. Zone 7.

H.'Mauvena'

This shrub was recorded in Watson's Nursery Catalogue in 1920, and as this nursery is in Killiney, Co. Dublin, an Irish origin is a possibility. It is a hybrid from H.'Andersonii', but has smaller leaves and deeper coloured flowers. It is said to be hardier than its parent.

A rounded shrub, much branched, growing to 60 in (150 cm) in height. The branchlets are green, becoming greeny brown and slightly pubescent. The leaves are mid green, lighter underneath, duller than the parent, up to 3 in (7.5 cm) in length and 1 in (2.5 cm) wide. The leaf blade is oblong lanceolate and in narrowing towards the stem tends to form shoulders on each side of a channelled stalk. The flowers are purple in colour fading white, and are held losely in spikes 3½–4 in (9–10 cm) long. Summer flowering.

A shrub for the back of the border. Zone 9.

H.'Mauve Queen'

A cultivar grown in Guernsey, Channel Islands, possibly a H.speciosa hybrid, that could have wider appeal for gardens near the sea, in Britain.

Well branched with upright yet rounded habit of growth, to a height of 54 in (137 cm). The branchlets are light green with brown nodes. The leaves are elliptic to obovate, at times mauvy purple leaf margins and midribs on the slightly paler under surface. The leaves close to the growing bud or covering it are also suffused mauvy purple beneath. The leaf blade is 2½ in (6.5 cm) long and up to 1 in (2.5 cm) wide and mid green in colour. Mauvy purple flowers are carried on spikes up to 3 in (7.5 cm) in length, in summer.

An attractive coastal garden shrub. Zone 9.

H.'Midsummer Beauty'

This popular cultivar was raised at Seaford, East Sussex at the end of the World War II and distributed by Messrs Cheals of Crawley, East Sussex. A cross between *H.*'Miss E. Fittall' and *H.speciosa* producing a showy shrub.

An erect, much branched, rounded shrub, growing to over 60 in (150 cm) in height. The branchlets are plum coloured (reddish brown) with darker nodes. The leaves are oblong lanceolate, 3½–4½ in (9–11.5 cm) and ¾ in (2 cm) in width. The leaf blade is matt green in colour with a paler under surface, which in young leaves is suffused plum colour and so, too, is the midrib. Veining is noticeable on the upper surface. The leaves are spreading and slightly down turning. Lilac purple flowers are displayed on 5–6 in (12.5–15 cm) spikes from midsummer into autumn.

A large, attractive shrub for the border. Zone 9; could be Zone 8 in southern England.

H.'Milborne Port'

A hardy shrub found growing in Somerset. Efforts to trace its name have led to Milborne Port near Sherborne, Dorset, but the raiser can not be found or its name, so this cultivar has been given the name of 'Milborne Port'.

A much branched, rounded shrub growing to a height of 60 in (150 cm). The branchlets are greeny brown and darker at the nodes. The leaves are glossy green, lanceolate 2–3 in (5–7.5 cm) in length and up to ¾ in (2 cm) wide. The leaves are upward growing and paler below.

Bluey mauve flowers are carried on spikes 3–4 in (7.5–10 cm) in length. The flowers fade white. The spikes appear towards the ends of the branchlets in July and go on appearing till March of the next year.

A hardy long flowering shrub; as background provides a foil for early summer flowering plants then comes into its own with winter and autumn flower.

Zone 8.

H.'Milmont Emerald'

A synonymous name for *H.*'Emerald Green', which see.

H.'Miss E. Fittall'

This wind resistant shrub was raised by Mr A. Andrews, the Parks Superintendent of Plymouth, Devon, before World War II and named after the Town Clerk's daughter, Miss Eleanor Fittall. It is another of the *H.speciosa* and *H.salicifolia* crosses and in its turn the parent of *H.*'Midsummer Beauty' and the Wand group of Hebes produced by Treseders of Truro, Cornwall.

An erect well branched, rounded shrub growing to over 60 in (150 cm) tall. The branchlets are greeny brown with brown nodes. The leaves are mid green not shiny, but paler beneath. The leaf blade is lanceolate to oblong lanceolate, 3–4 in (7.5–10 cm) in length and ¾ in (2 cm) wide.

The leaves are spreading and down turning at the tips.

Spikes of bluey mauve flowers, up to 6 in (15 cm) in length including the 1 in (2.5 cm) stalk, appear in summer towards the ends of the branchlets. There is usually a slight wave in the spike two-thirds of its length from the stem.

Used as a hedging or background shrub. Zone 8.

H. 'Mrs E. Tennant'

H. 'Miss Lowe'

8.10 H.*'Mrs E. Tennant'*, H.*'Miss Lowe'*

H.'Miss Lowe'

A neater growing cultivar of *H.*'Great Orme', which was raised at the Guernsey home of Earl Poulett. He also lived at Hinton St George in Somerset, where Miss Dorothy Lowe (1908–1976) lived at the Malt House and after whom this Hebe is named.

A much branched, fairly compact, rounded shrub growing to a height of 48 in (120 cm). The branchlets are greeny brown with purplish brown nodes. The leaves are shiny green, duller beneath; length 2 in (5 cm); width 3/10 in (8 mm). The leaf blade is oblong elliptic and those near the growth buds are suffused purple on the under surface. Bright pink flowers, in 1½–2 in (4–5 cm) spikes, on 3/4 in (2 cm) stalks, appear in early and late summer.

Another useful shrub for the more sheltered or coastal garden. Zone 9 or Zone 10.

H.'Mont Blanc'

Named after the famous mountain and that is all that is known about its origin.

99

A rounded shrub, well branched, fairly erect and growing to a height of 60 in (150 cm). Its branchlets are light greeny brown, and it has a large leaf bud sinus. The leaves are yellow green, lanceolate narrowing towards the stem, slightly shiny, 1½–2 in (4–5 cm) long and ½–¾ in (1.25–2 cm) wide. The leaves are upward growing. White flowers with brown anthers are carried on spikes 3–4 in (7.5–10 cm) in length, in summer and again in autumn. The flowers appear towards the end of the branchlets and are long flowering.

A good border shrub with its flowering and its lighter foliage as a foil for other shrubs. Hardiness a little suspect in unprotected sites. Zone 10.

H.'Monticola'

Although 'monticola' means mountain loving, this is not a plant for growing on mountains, in Britain or elsewhere. This name is also a synonym for *H.subalpina* and the Registrar is suggesting that *H.*'Monticola' is changed. (A suggestion for a name — 'Monte Carlo'!)

This is another *H.*'Carnea' cultivar, so it is fairly erect, yet spreading, well branched; height 48 in (120 cm). The branchlets are light brown, deepening with age. The leaves are yellow green, shiny, duller below. The leaf blade is 1¾–2½ in (4.5–6.5 cm) in length and ⅖ in (1 cm) in width. The leaves are narrow lanceolate, spreading and downturning; the leaf surface is sometimes undulating. Light pink flowers in spikes, 2½ in (6.5 cm) long, appear in summer.

Another flowering shrub for the more sheltered garden in the south or south west of Britain or by the coast. Zone 9.

H.'Morning Clouds'

A hybrid from *H.*'Youngii' with the other parent possibly *H.pimeleoides* var. *glaucocaerulea*. Raised at County Park Nursery, Essex.

Loosely spreading branches upturning at the ends, brown in colour and only a few inches (cm) in height. The leaves are ovate, slightly concave, the margins tending to be purplish green, up to ½ in (1.25 cm) in length and ¼ in (6 mm) in width. The leaf blade is glaucous green above and glossy green below. The leaf bud has a sinus. Bluey mauve flowers are freely produced in midsummer on racemes three times the length of the leaves.

A rock garden plant or plant for the front of a small border. Zone 8, or Zone 9 in exposed areas.

H.'Mrs E. Tennant'

Where this cultivar originated has not been traced.

A rounded, branched shrub. The green branchlets grow to a height of up to 24 in (60 cm); no nodal ring. The leaves are obovate and narrowing towards the stem; length 2 in (5 cm); width ½ in (1.25 cm). The leaf blade is dark green and shiny, the lower surface paler. The midrib can be purplish towards the stem. The leaves are fairly close together and tend to turn in one plane. The leaf bud has a small sinus.

Bluey mauve flowers in 2–3 in (5–7.5 cm) spikes, appear near the ends of the stems, in summer.

A pleasant cultivar for the south and west. Zone 9.

H.'Mrs Winder'

A popular cultivar for its foliage especially in winter, but its origin can not be traced.

A dense, much branched shrub, rounded and growing to about 36 in (90 cm). The branchlets are brown with darker brown nodes. The leaves are dark green, oblong elliptic, narrowing to the tip up to $1\frac{1}{2}$ in (4 cm) in length and $\frac{4}{10}$ in (1 cm) in width; the leaf blade is slightly concave. The leaves at the ends of the stems have reddish brown midribs and leaf margins. The leaves surrounding the growing bud often turn pinkish in colder weather in winter; also the leaf margins and midrib can bronze. Violet flowers in spikes $2\frac{1}{2}$–3 in (6.5–7.5 cm) long appear in late summer towards the ends of the branchlets.

A cultivar well worth growing for its foliage alone. Zone 9, or even Zone 8 in some more sheltered sites.

H.'Myrtifolia' (IS)

The *Veronica myrtifolia* of Banks and Solander from North Auckland, North Island, NZ and which Hook said was a variety of *H.macrocarpa*. Bentham's description of later specimens said they were like *V.salicifolia*. Until it is re-discovered, it must remain an uncertain species. The description spoke of short, broad leaves and large white flowers.

H.'Neil's Choice'

Possibly a hybrid from one of the bronze leaved Hebes, like *H.*'Eversley Seedling'. It grows to 3–4 ft (90–120 cm) in height and is worth growing for its good reddish foliage in winter. Raised at County Park Nursery, Essex, it has short spikes of violet flowers in summer. Flowering continues into autumn and even winter. Zone 8 or Zone 9.

H.'Nicola's Blush'

A low growing cultivar, recently introduced by County Park Nursery, Essex, about which little is known as to how it came to be raised. What is known is that it is long flowering, from June to November, the pleasant light pink flowers gradually turn white and produce a two colour effect. This could be an attractive newer Hebe for the garden. Zone 8 or Zone 9.

H.'Obovata' (IS)

Mention can be made of this glabrous and woody shrub found by Broken River in Canterbury, South Island, NZ, but it is still uncertain as to whether it is a species. The shrub is erect and grows to 48–60 in (120–150 cm) in height. The branches are stout and later marked with scars of fallen leaves. The leaves are obovate, the margins tend to be thickened and the leaf blade is slightly concave; length 1 in (2.5 cm); width $\frac{1}{2}$ in (1.25 cm). The leaf bud is without a sinus. White flowers appear in short spikes, 1¼–1½ in (3–4 cm) long.

Possibly not yet in cultivation in Britain. Zone 8 or Zone 7.

H.obtusata

(Latin — obtusus = blunt or rounded at the ends, or obtuse). A semi-prostrate shrub from the Auckland Province west coast from Manakau Heads to Muriwai, North Island, NZ.

As in the wild, where it grows on the cliffs, this shrub ground covers or grows over rocks or rocky banks, growing up to 24 in (60 cm) and is spreading. The branchlets are reddish or purple. The leaves are green, paler beneath, obovate to oblong in shape and rounded at the ends, hence its name. Length 1–2 in (2.5–5 cm); width ½–1 in (1.25–2.5 cm). The leaves are spreading more or less in one plane. Lavender mauve flowers are held in spikes twice the length of the leaves. Long flowering from summer into autumn of the well displayed flowers.

The species is a little variable, so by careful selection this could become a very useful coastal shrub. Zone 9.

H.ochracea

(Latin — ochracea = ochre coloured). The name aptly describes this rounded shrub found in the mountains of western Nelson Province and Cobb Valley, South Island, NZ.

A rather rigid, branched, rounded shrub, growing up to 42 in (105 cm). The branchlets are slightly four-sided, olive green below and ochre coloured at the tips. Being whipcord, the leaves, which are ochre-green to ochre-brown, are very small, deltoid in shape, thick and pressed to the stem, as well as being joined at the base and for one-third of their length, which is 1/20–1/12 in (1–1.5 mm). The small, white flowers are carried in short spikes of up to ten flowers in May and June, towards the ends of the branchlets.

A useful foliage shrub for the shrub border. Zone 7.

H.ochracea 'James Stirling'

A low, spreading and much branched and much brighter cultivar of H.ochracea introduced by James Stirling, past Superintendent of Grounds of Parliament Buildings, Wellington, NZ. This whipcord has the same very small leaves pressed to the stems, the branchlets are yellowish green, otherwise the description is the same as for H.ochracea. It would seem to be a brighter, more yellow green, more spreading variety of H.ochracea. Zone 7.

H.odora

(Latin — odora = a pleasant smell) Known as the 'Boxwood' because of its habit of growth, it is to be found in the mountain regions of both North and South Islands, Stewart and Auckland Islands, NZ, usually in wet ground and up to an altitude of 4,500 ft (1,371 m).

A rounded, ball shaped bush though rather variable in growth in the wild. Grows slowly up to 48–54 in (120–137 cm). The branchlets are green to yellowish green. The leaves are dark green, shiny above, dull and paler below. The leaf blade is elliptic ovate and up to ³/₄ in (2 cm) in length and ³/₁₀ in (8 mm) in width. The flowers appear in late spring in terminal spikes of not many white flowers, with one or two pairs of lateral spikes from the leaf axils below the growing bud, so forming a conical flower head.

An interesting shrub for the garden, as it will grow in most soils and positions. Zone 7.

H.odora cultivars

In Britain, there are two cultivars which are problematical. The first is H.'Anomala', which is green in colour and not the H.'Anomala' discovered by J.F. Armstrong in the head waters of the Rakaia Valley, South Island, NZ in 1865 which has shining dark green leaf tips to the branchlets and is described under H.'Anomala', which see.

The other is H.'Buxifolia', taller, more erect, not so globular and branched at the ends of the branchlets. In H.odora, leaves are at right angles to the branches, whereas in H.'Buxifolia' they are upturned at an angle of 45° to the stem. In H.odora the yellow green leaves are concave, yellow green margined and with a short petiole or stalk. In H.'Buxifolia' the leaves are more pointed, flat to very slightly concave, with a light green margin and only half the size. The stems are half the thickness and the new branchlets occur in clusters terminally, but not in H.odora. The leaves are sessile in H.'Buxifolia'. So, are they the same as we are asked to accept?

H.odora 'New Zealand Gold'

In the *Hebe News*, Vol. 2 No. 5 (Dec. 1987) Kenneth A. Beckett of Stanhoe, Norfolk, writes that he collected this Hebe in the Arthur's Pass area of the Southern Alps, South Island, NZ. It seemed to be an extra bushy and shapely specimen of H.odora but subsequently was found to have yellow tips to the shoots, so he named it H.odora 'New Zealand Gold'.

Upright growing to 42 in (105 cm) becoming wider as it branches which can result in bare lower branches if this is not watched. The stems are yellow green. The leaves are glossy, dark green, ovate and ¹/₂ in (1.25 cm) in length, ¹/₅ in (5 mm) in width. The short leaf stalk clings to the stem for ¹/₅ in (5 mm), then the leaf blade spreads away from the stem. The bud at the end of the branchlet is gold coloured and the leaves around it are gold tipped. The margin around the leaf is also yellow. There are 1–2 short spikes of white flowers arising in the axils of the leaves at the top of the stem, and these are surmounted by a terminal spike, so making a cone of flowers. Flowers late spring.

An eye catching cultivar for which you may have to search. It is not easy to propagate and a best way needs to be found. Zone 7.

H.odora 'Wintergreen'

An upright, neat growing shrub which differs from H.odora 'New Zealand Gold' in the following ways: no gold tipping and the end of the branchlets which are more green; the leaf is attached in the same way to the stem, but is not so shiny, has no yellow margin and is duller beneath. The size is also slightly smaller; length ⅖ in (1 cm); width ⅕ in (5 mm).

A foliage shrub coming into its own in winter. Not so difficult to propagate. Zone 7.

H.'Orientale'

A cultivar of unknown origin which makes a low growing, spreading shrub, yet tends to grow erect. The branchlets are brown and it grows up to 9 in (22.5 cm). The leaves are obovate, upturning at the margins and the petioles clasp the stem. The leaf colour is mid green with a hint of purple; the main rib on the under surface is prominent. The leaf length is ½ in (1.25 cm); width ¼ in (6 mm). Small, off white (white with a hint of brown) flowers appear in short spikes towards the ends of the branchlets, in summer.

A rock garden shrub. Zone 8.

H.'Page Boy'

A green leaved form of H.'Pagei', which was raised from seed of H.'Pagei' at County Park Nursery, Essex. See the parent plant for the description of other features.

H.'Pagei'

Edward Page, a native of Sussex, England, went to New Zealand in 1912 and became Foreman of Dunedin Botanic Garden, South Island, NZ. At that Botanic Garden there is a record of Veronica 'Pagei' growing in the Garden in 1926, but no details of its origin. Most likely it is a cultivar from Hart and Darton and their garden at Weatherstones, Lawrence, Otago, South Island. H.pinguifolia is a parent of this hybrid.

A low growing, carpeting shrub with brown branchlets, which are purplish at first. Height a few inches (cm). The leaves are slightly concave, obovate, rounded and spreading. The glaucous grey, slightly pubescent leaf blade is lighter green at the margin and duller below; length up to ½ in (1.25 cm); width ¼ in (6 mm). Because it is carpeting, the leaves tend to flatten into one plane. Short spikes of pearly white flowers appear in May. The spikes, ¾–1 in (2–2.5 cm) long, are carried towards the ends of the branchlets.

A very popular Hebe for rock gardens, troughs and front of the border. Does best in a sunny position. Zone 7.

H.pareora

A small shrub that comes from the Upper Pareora River, a few other streams on the Hunters Hills and the gorge of the Opihi River, South Island, NZ. Botanists had said that H.amplexicaulis was the same as

H.pareora and should be given that name. The latest news is that they are not the same and that *H.amplexicaulis* does not come from the localities given above. Until the botanical differences become known in Britain, use the descriptions for *H.amplexicaulis* as a guide.

H.parviflora

A variable species found in scrubland, along streamsides and forest margins in North and South Islands, NZ and from sea level to 2,000 feet (610 m).

A much branched shrub or small tree, in height from 6 ft (1.8 m) to 20 ft (6.1 m) and from compact to more open. So for the garden look for the lower growing, compact forms. The branchlets are yellow green with darker nodes. The leaves are linear lanceolate, stiff with a smooth glabrous surface. The narrow leaf blades are 1–2½ in (2.5–6.5 cm) long and ⅙–¼ in (4–6 mm) in width. The leaf bud is without a sinus. White flowers, in spikes 2½ in (6.5 cm) in summer in the upper leaf axils of the stems.

If a compact form cannot be found, then grow the variety *angustifolia*. Zone 8.

H.parviflora var. *angustifolia*

From the Nelson and Marlborough Regions of South Island, NZ, where it grows in rocky places, in river valleys and along forest margins. Not so tall as *H.parviflora*.

Much branched, fairly compact, upright growing to a height of 36–48 in (90–120 cm). The branchlets are yellow brown in colour carrying pairs of leaves widely spaced apart. The leaves are narrow, linear lanceolate, dark green in colour, spreading and often drooping and rather sickle shaped; length 1½–3½ in (6–9 cm); width ⅙–¼ in (4–6 mm). The leaf blade is shining above and paler below. Slender, slightly drooping spikes, 2–5 in (5–12.5 cm) long, of loosely spaced white or bluish white flowers, appear in summer.

An attractive shrub for the garden; quite hardy. Zone 7.

H.parviflora var. *arborea*

Can make a rounded tree up to 20 ft (6.1 m) in height or more in its native home on the hillsides above Wellington, North Island, NZ. It has yet to be discovered how it will grow in Britain. The leaves are linear lanceolate, 1–1⅖ in (2.5–3.5 cm) long and 3/16 in (4 mm) wide either erect or spreading. The spikes are densely packed with white flowers, in summer. Zone 8.

H.pauciflora

As the Latin name suggests, there are few flowers produced on the prostrate branches, that ascend at the tips of this small, closely branched shrub, which is found on open grassy areas above 3,000 ft (914 m) on the Fiordland Mts, South Island, NZ. This Hebe looks like a very small form of *H.odora*. The leaves are glossy, spoon shaped, overlapping and later more spreading. The leaf blade is ¼ in (6 mm) long and 3/16 in (4 mm) wide. A pair of spikes of white flowers, ⅖ in (1 cm) long, appear just below the growing bud on the branchlets. There are two flowers in each spikelet, which look large for the size of plant.

An alpine plant, possibly not in Britain. What you may see is the cultivar with the same name, which is next described. Zone 7.

H.'Pauciflora'

A hybrid of the cultivar H.'Christensenii, which was H.odora crossed with an unknown whipcord and named after Mr C.E. Christensen, who collected plants with Dr L. Cockayne in the Hanmer District. In the case of H.'Pauciflora', it is again a whipcord hybrid and it is understood that it was introduced by Messrs Blooms of Bressingham, Norfolk.

Forms a mounded bush, much branched with upward growing branches to a height of 18 in (45 cm). The branchlets are green and give a two colour effect with the deeper green leaves. The way the branchlets arise is typical of H.'Christensenii' — up the branch a group of branchlets arise, then a gap and another group of branchlets arise and so on up the branch. The branchlets follow this same pattern. Branchlets usually arise opposite each other, but one finds only branchlets on one side, perhaps 2–3, and then back to normal. This pattern is again followed on the branchlet itself. The leaves are erect to slightly spreading, one pair over-lapping over the bases of the next, dark green and shining above, slightly paler below. The leaf blade is concave above, oblong ovate, ⅛ in (3 mm) in length and 1/16 in (1.5 mm) wide. The flowers are hardly ever seen, but are white in colour.

Hardy, but does not tolerate prolonged drought or dry conditions, otherwise a useful cultivar to include amongst the other whipcords for a colour contrast. Quite a pleasing cultivar with its rounded growth, as it spreads as wide as it grows tall. Zone 8.

(Note: The details were taken from the actual shrub and there is so little difference between this cultivar and H.'Christensenii' that they could be said to be the same, so resolving the problem of a species and cultivar with the same name.)

H.pauciramosa

The Latin name pauciramosa suggests that the stems are little or poorly branched, and this is so. H.pauciramosa is found widely in wet ground in the mountains of Canterbury, Otago and Southland, South Island, NZ. There is a form or variety called masonae named after Miss Ruth Mason, who collected in the Nelson Mts District, South Island and this is recog-nised as a distinct form with quadrangular branches.

A shrub rounded in outline, with erect branches mostly arising from the base growing up to a height of about 20 in (50 cm). The branches are mid green in colour. The leaves are concave, slightly shiny on both surfaces, erect at first then spreading. The leaf blade is broadly oblong, up to ¼ in (6 mm) in length and 3/16 in (4 mm) wide. The leaf colour is dark green and lighter on the margins. Short spikes, about ¾ in (2 cm) in length, are crowded with white flowers in June, near the branch tips.

With its neat growth, it is useful for edging borders or growing in rock gardens. It looks like a smaller form of *H.odora* and could do well in a trough. Zone 7.

H.'Penny Day'

Little is known about this small leaved Hebe, recently catalogued by County Park Nursery, Essex. It is a free flowering cultivar, with short racemes of lilac pink flowers in summer. Zone 9, possibly.

H.'Petra's Pink'

A low growing Hebe, height about 12 in (30 cm), raised at County Park Nursery, Essex. All that is known about this cultivar is that it is the first small leaved Hebe with pale pink flowers. Zone 9, possibly.

H.petriei

Named after the Scottish-born Donald Petrie (1846–1925), a botanist and plant collector. This is a mountain species.

A many branched, woody shrub, tending to be decumbent in growth, to a height of 20 in (50 cm). The glabrous stems are almost hidden by the leaves, which are obovate spathulate, glabrous green and spreading; length ¼ in (6–9 mm) or more; width ¹⁄₁₀–¹⁄₅ in (2–5 mm). Small, white flowers appear in a compact terminal spike, in summer. The spike is cylindrical about 2 in (5 cm) long.

H.petriei comes from the mountains near Lake Wakitipu and is found in rocky debris, whereas *H.petriei* var. *murrellii*, named after Leslie A. Murrell (1892–1953), is found in the Kepler Range near Fowler Pass, Lake Manapouri, South Island, NZ. Only minor botanical differences in flower and leaves separates the variety from the species. Zone 7; not in Britain yet.

H.'Pewter Dome'

A hybrid from *H.albicans*, but who raised it is not known; it is thought to be a seedling.

A grey leaved, rounded or dome shaped bush, much branched and growing up to 15 in (37 cm) in height, with a similar spread or slightly more. The branchlets are brown in colour and close together, The leaves are greeny grey, ovate oblong, ⅖ in (2 cm) in length and ⅖ in (1 cm) in width; glaucous below. White flowers in short, pointed spikes up to 1 in (2.5 cm) in length appear in the axils of the leaves below the growing bud on the branchlets, in late May and early June. The pedicel is ½ in (1,.25 cm) in length, so carrying the flowers beyond the leaves.

A very good garden shrub for borders or rock gardens. Zone 7.

H.pimeleoides

As the name infers, it is like the Pimelea, another genus of evergreen New Zealand and Australian shrubs and herbs. *H.pimeleoides* is found east of the main divide on the mountains from Marlborough to South Canterbury, South Island, NZ and generally in the drier regions. It has transferred well to cultivation in the garden, appreciating drier soil and a sunny position on the rock garden or trough.

A more or less prostrate shrub with dark, purplish stems, growing from 3 in (7.5 cm) up to 12 in (30 cm). The leaves are narrow lanceolate to ovate, glaucous, spreading; length up to ³/₁₀ in (8 mm); width ¹/₁₀ in (2 mm). The leaf margins are yellowish, sometimes reddish; no sinus. Bluish purple flowers appear in summer, in fairly long racemes.

A worthwhile shrub for the rock garden. Zone 7.

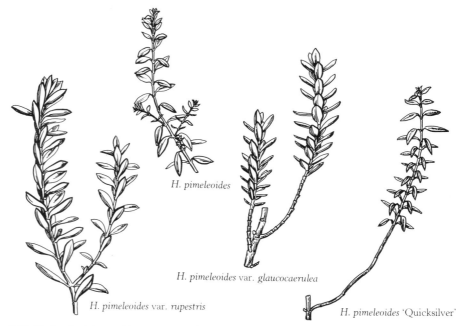

H. pimeleoides

H. pimeleoides var. *glaucocaerulea*

H. pimeleoides var. *rupestris*

H. pimeleoides 'Quicksilver'

8.11 H.pimeleoides *and its varieties and cultivars:* H.pimeleoides *var.* glaucocaerulea, H.pimeleoides *'Quicksilver'*, H.pimeleoides *var.* rupestris

H.pimeleoides var. glaucocaerulea

Found by J.B. Armstrong, Curator of Christchurch Botanic Garden, in the Upper Rakaia and Upper Rangitata River valleys, South Island, NZ, and most plants in cultivation today seem to have descended from Armstrong's original plants. The name indicates a greyish blue bloom (leaves).

An erect shrub with stouter branches and fairly open growth, to a height of 18 in (45 cm). The branchlets are purplish brown changing to brown with slightly deeper brown nodes. The leaves are ovate and upward growing, tending to spread later. The leaf blade tends to be rather thick, glaucous grey on both surfaces, margins yellowish to purplish red; length ¼–½ in (6–12.5 mm); width ¼ in (6 mm). Violet blue flowers appear in summer in short spikes, ½ in (1.25 cm) long, carried on stalks up to ¾ in (2 cm) in length, towards the ends of the branchlets.

An interesting shrub for the flower arranger and for providing a different colour and texture in the border or rock garden. Zone 7.

H.pimeleoides 'Quicksilver'

This cultivar, introduced by County Park Nursery, Essex, differs from *H.pimeleoides* in having leaves half the length but the same width and an attractive grey in colour.

A much branched spreading plant; the spread can be as much as 30 in (75 cm) and height up to 18 in (45 cm). The stems are purplish brown with darker nodes. The leaves are elliptic to rounded, held at right angles to the stem; length ³⁄₁₆ in (4 mm); width ¹⁄₁₀ in (2 mm). The leaf blade is glaucous and very intense grey, justifying the name of 'Quicksilver'. The flowers are similar in colour (bluish purple) to the parent, in racemes of fair length, in summer.

A plant for gardeners and flower arrangers. A sunny position will bring out the colour of the leaves. Zone 8.

H.pimeleoides var. *rupestris*

This variety is commonly found in Central Otago, South Island, NZ growing on rocks, hence the name 'rupestris'. At the time of writing, I have been informed by the Registrar that learned opinion considers this may be a distinct species, but as yet it has not been re-named.

More spreading than other species and varieties with glabrous dark brown branchlets; height up to 18 in (45 cm). The leaves are broad elliptic, glaucous on both surfaces with yellow green margins, spreading but upward growing at first; length ⅖ in (1 cm); width ³⁄₁₆ in (4 mm) — can be slightly larger. Mauve flowers ageing to white appear on short spikes, in summer.

An attractive plant for the shrub border or rock garden. Do not be put off by the not so highly coloured flowers. Zone 8.

H.pinguifolia

(Latin — pinguis = fatty or greasy; refers to the leaves in this species) Found in subalpine scrub and rocks on the eastern mountains from Marlborough to South Canterbury, South Island, NZ.

A small decumbent shrub up to 9 in (22.5 cm) in height with fairly stout branches. The branchlets are greeny brown in colour, with brown nodes. The leaves are broadly ovate, concave, glaucous with lighter green or reddish margins. Upward growing at first, becoming wide spread or even slightly down turning. Length of leaf blade ⅖ in (1 cm); width ⅕ in (5 mm). The leaf bud is without a sinus. White flowers are carried in densely packed spikes up to ½ in (1.25 cm) long, on stalks of about the same length. The flowers usually appear in June, near the ends of the stems.

A mountain plant growing above 2,500 ft (610 m), hence its popularity as a rock garden plant. Zone 7.

H.pinguifolia'Forma'

This is a neater, denser form of H.pinguifolia. The branchlets appear thinner and are lighter brown, even purplish at first. The leaves are not so concave or thick as the leaves of the parent. The length is about the same but the width is ½₀ in (1 mm) less. The leaves on the branchlets are also shorter by the same amount.

For other details, see parent plant.

H.pinguifolia'Sutherlandii'

A selected, more decumbent and spreading form of H.pinguifolia, which in the wild is a very variable species. The branchlets are ascending and fairly close and stouter. The leaves are spreading, ovate to rounded, less glaucous, but still with yellow green margins; length ⅓ in (8 mm); width ¼ in (6 mm). The leaf blade is slightly concave, grey green. Where the leaves join the stem, the nodal ring is purplish brown. White flowers which, like the parent, appear in short, densely packed spikes, in summer.

A good ground coverer as it can spread up to 36 in (90 cm) across, growing to a height of 15 in (37 cm). Zone 7.

H.'Pink Wand'

One of the 'Wand' group of hybrids raised from H.'Miss E. Fittall' by Treseders of Truro, Cornwall.

A slightly different member of the group, a much branched, rounded shrub growing to 54–60 in (135–150 cm). The branchlets are green with light brown nodes. The leaves are oblong lanceolate, up to 3½ in (9 cm) in length and ½–¾ in (1.25–2 cm) wide. The leaf blade is green, slightly shiny but duller and paler on the underside. Bright pink flowers appear in spikes up to 4 in (10 cm) long, in summer.

Not quite so hardy as the other 'Wands', but still an attractive cultivar for the shrub border in the sheltered, warmer garden. Zone 10.

H.'Polden Hills'

A seedling from H.'Great Orme', occurring in 1975 and named after the hills, on which it first grew, at Polden Acres, Somerset. It was retained because of the flower colour.

A moderately branched, fairly upright, rounded shrub growing to a height of 42 in (105 cm). The branchlets are green with a brown nodal ring. The leaves are green, narrow lanceolate up to 2½ in (6.5 cm) long and ⅖ in (1 cm) wide, the leaves becoming less in length and width towards the top of the branchlets. The leaf blade is shiny, paler underneath. The flowers are rose pink, so differing from other H. 'Carnea' cultivars. The spikes carrying the flowers can reach 4–5 in (10–12.5 cm) in length and appear in the axils of the leaves just below the growing bud, in summer. There can be up to three pairs of spikes to a stem.

Given a sheltered site or coastal garden, this cultivar can make a pleasant border shrub. Zone 9.

H.'Polly Moore'

This cultivar seems to be a dwarf form of H.'Autumn Glory' growing to about 12 in (30 cm) tall. The origin is not known.

A small rounded shrub with upward growing branches. The branchlets are reddish brown. The leaves are dark green, paler below, up to $^7/_{10}$ in (1.7 cm) in length and $^3/_{10}$ in (8 mm) in width. The leaf blade is obovate and elliptic ovate on the same shrub, as with H. 'Autumn Glory'. There are reddish margins to the leaves. Short spikes of violet flowers appear towards the ends of the branchlets, in summer.

A useful cultivar, where a small shrub is needed for a trough or tub. Be patient, it is slow growing. Zone 9.

H.poppelwellii

A small, erect, tufted shrub of the whipcord group, named after Dugald. L. Poppelwell (1863–1929), solicitor and botanist, who took George Biggar on his plant collecting excursions, such as to the Garvie Mts, South Island, NZ where this whipcord Hebe is to be found.

This erect shrub forms tufts 3–6 in (7–15 cm) in height. The branchlets are rather thin and shiny. The leaves are very small, deltoid, joined for one-third of their length, then mostly pressed to the stem. White flowers appear in spikes, about $^2/_5$ in in length, with up to 15 flowers in a spike, in June. Can be reluctant to flower.

This species has a four-sided arrangement of its very small leaves, which are pressed against the stems giving a glossy green appearance. A rock plant. Zone 7.

H.'Primley Gem'

This cultivar was raised in the gardens of Paignton Zoo in Devon. The cultivars H.'Margery Fish', H.'Morning Glory' and H.'Primley Blue' are synonymous.

A compact, rounded shrub, to a height of 30 in (75 cm) with reddish brown branchlets, which tend to crowd the bush. The nodes are slightly darker. The leaf blade margin down turns from the stem end, on both sides, to a third of the length of the leaf. The margins and the leaf flatten out, thus giving the wave distinctive to this cultivar. The leaf blade is ovate elliptic, dark green, lighter beneath, and has a reddish margin; length $^3/_4$– 1 in (2–2.5 cm); width $^4/_{10}$ in (1 cm) where the leaf forms wave. The growing bud and the under surfaces of the leaves around it are also reddish. Mauvy blue flowers are carried on spikes up to $2^1/_2$ in (6.5 cm) long with a stalk 1 in (2.5 cm) in length. The flowers appear at the tops of the branchlets in summer and later.

A useful shrub for the border both for foliage and flower. Zone 9; or Zone 8 away from cold winds and severe frosts.

H.'Princess'

A neat, dome shaped, semi whipcord Hebe growing to about 6 in (15 cm) in height. Found growing in 1985 at Bath, near Lake Tennyson, South Island, NZ by County Park Nursery, at Essex.

H.propinqua

The Latin word propinquus means near in relationship, and refers to this species' early confusion with *H.salicornioides*. Mats of *H.propinqua* are freely found in peaty grassland in subalpine regions from 2,500–5,000 ft (792–1,525 m) from Southland to South Canterbury, South Island, NZ. *N.propinqua* belongs to the whipcord group.

A much branched shrub forming a mat over 3 ft (90 cm) across, in the wild. The branches are spreading, the branchlets are short, either spreading or erect, light to yellow green in colour. The leaves are very small, light yellow green, ovate and adpressed to the stem, joined at the base for one-third to one-half of their length. The leaf blade is about $\frac{1}{20}$ in (2 mm) in length. Spikes of 12 white flowers appear towards the ends of the branchlets, in summer.

A very good ground covering shrub, much used in New Zealand, but slow in being used in British gardens. In cultivation it is no more than 12 in (30 cm) in height and up to 24 in (60 cm) across. Ideal for rock gardens, preferring a moist soil. Zone 7.

H.'Prostrata'

With leaves tending to overlap and form in one plane, *H.chathamica* has been suggested as one parent and *H.canterburiensis* as the other parent, but stem, leaf shape and colour do not fit. This makes *H.odora* a more likely suggestion except for stem colour; and this leaves *H.vernicosa* with more related colour and leaf shape.

A spreading, ground covering plant, to a height of a few inches (cm). The greeny brown branchlets have darker nodes. The leaves are obovate to elliptic, dark green, glossy; length $\frac{2}{5}$ in (1 cm); width $\frac{1}{5}$ in (5 mm). Duller under the leaf blade, which is spreading. Short spikes of white flowers appear in summer.

An interesting shrub for covering the rocks. Zone 8.

H.pubescens

(Latin — pubescens = clad in short soft hairs) The branchlets, pale green above and bronze below, are covered in fine, soft hairs. This straggly branched shrub grows in the wild to 72 in (180 cm) tall. This species comes from Mercury Bay on the Coramandel Peninsula, North Island, NZ. The leaves, too, are spreading, up to 3½ in (9 cm) in length and ¾ in (2 cm) in width. The leaf blade is mid green, oblong lanceolate, almost ear shaped, with the under surface almost covered in fine hairs, with longer hairs around the margin and along the midrib. White or lavender flowers are closely set in racemes near the ends of the branchlets.

A most curious Hebe; not for garden cultivation. Zone 9.

H.'Purple Picture'

An upright growing shrub reaching 42–48 in (105–120 cm) in height, with purplish leaves, paler beneath. 2–3 in (5–7.5 cm) racemes or spikes of purple flowers appear in summer and well into autumn. Introduced by County Park Nursery, Essex. Zone 9, or possibly Zone 8.

H.'Purple Princess'

An erect shrub growing up to 36 in (90 cm), with reddish green stems. The green leaves have reddish margins and midrib as well as the base of the leaf. Spikes of bluey purple flowers appear in summer. Another County Park Nursery, Essex introduction. Zone 9, possibly.

H.'Purple Queen'

A typical *H.speciosa* hybrid of unknown origin. H.'Royal Glory' and H.'Purple Splendour' are supposed to be better forms of H.'Purple Queen'.

A shrub of compact habit, well branched, fairly upright growing to a height of 54 in (135 cm). The branchlets are bronzed, so too is the growing bud. The leaves are obovate elliptic, upward growing, up to 2 in (5 cm) in length, ¾ in (2 cm) in width. The leaf blade is dark green, shiny; the lower surface has a bronzed midrib. On leaves around the growing point, the underside is deeply bronzed, fading as the leaves grow. 2–3 in (5–7.5 cm). Spikes of violet purple flowers are carried on 1 in (2.5 cm) stalks, in summer.

A shrub for coastal or warmer gardens inland or grow in pots or tubs to enjoy the foliage and flowers of this half hardy cultivar. Zone 9 (10).

H.'Purple Tips'

A variegated branch sport from H.'La Seduisante'. This sport has been called H.'Andersonii Tricolor' and *H.speciosa* 'Tricolor', but when the cultivar arrived in New Zealand it was at once identified as H.'Purple Tips' by the Registrar. (Our collection has been sent to New Zealand to help with the check list.)

A well branched, rounded shrub, fairly upright but only growing to 48 in (120 cm) being variegated. The branchlets are brown, but suffused plum near the tips. The leaves are variegated grey green, pale grey green almost cream along the margins of the leaves and when cold there is a suffusion of plum colour on both surfaces of the leaf. The leaf blade is ovate to elliptic, spreading, up to 2 in (5 cm) in length, width ¾–1 in (2–2.5 cm). The midribs, leaf under surface and growing bud at the tips of the shoots are suffused plum colour. Violet purple flowers are closely placed on spikes up to 3 in (7.5 cm) long, in summer — the same as the parent. H.'La Seduisante', which see for more detail.

113

This is a tender Hebe and only grown outside from late May to mid September. With its striking foliage and flowers, it is worth the extra trouble of overwintering in frost free conditions. An ideal shrub for tubs or large containers. Zone 10.

H.rakaiensis

A spreading shrub from the streamsides and rocky outcrops of the Rakaia Valley and from mid Canterbury, South Island, NZ southwards.

A much branched, bushy shrub, spreading as wide or wider than it grows tall, which is up to 24 in (60 cm). The stems are light brown with darker nodes soon ageing darker. There is an unnamed cultivar with golden stems and much taller growing that is sold as *H.rakaiensis*. The leaves are bright green, almost apple green, glossy, that turn more yellow in winter, especially in a sunny position. The leaf blade is obovate to oblong; length up to ¾ in (2 cm); width ¼ in (6 mm). White flowers on short spikes, 1–1½ in (2.5–4 cm) long, appear in late May, towards the ends of the shoots. The flowers just smother the bush.

An attractive and popular shrub for which a place could be found in most gardens. Zone 7.

H.rakaiensis 'Golden Dome'

A lower growing form of *H.rakaiensis*, at one time called *H.alpina* 'Golden Dome'. A much branched spreading, dome shaped Hebe growing to 18–20 in (45–50 cm) in height. All other features are the same as *H.rakaiensis*, even to the upward growing, glossy leaves and no leaf bud sinus.

H.ramosissima

(Latin — ramus = much branched) A small, fleshy leaved plant found in moist rocky debris on Mt. Tapaenuku, Marlborough, South Island, NZ.

Prostrate, mat forming up to 9 in (22.5 cm) and much branched. The leaves are spreading, broadly obovate, green, fleshy; length about ⅕ in (5 mm); width ¹⁄₁₀ in (2 mm). Terminal spikes of 2–4 white flowers appear in late spring or early summer.

A mountain plant not very widely known. Zone 7.

H.raoulii

Named after Edouard F.A. Raoul (1815–1852), the Medical Officer on *L'Aube*, Captain Lavaud's ship. This small plant is found straggling over rocks on the drier mountains of Canterbury, South Island, NZ above 500 ft (152 m).

A small, much branched shrub, straggling to more closely growing; a variable species growing to about 10 in (25 cm). The branchlets are purplish and pubescent. The leaves are small, leathery, mid green and spathula shaped with reddish margins; length variable ½–1 in (1.25–2.5 cm); width ⅛–³⁄₁₀ in (3–8 mm). There is slight toothing near the tip of the spreading leaves. Flowers appear in a terminal panicle up to 2–2¼ in (5–6 cm) long, in late spring. Lavender, sometimes pinkish, coloured flowers.

In the garden, this Hebe makes a more compact plant, which is ideal for the rock garden. When propagating, choose compact plants for cuttings or for seed. Seedlings should also be carefully examined and straggly plants removed. Zone 7.

H.raoulii var. *maccaskillii*

Found growing in the crevices in the limestone rocks of North Canterbury, it has slender branches and is more erect. The leaves are smaller, not so toothed and the white flowers are carried on one or two lateral spikes. Very hardy and another plant for the rock garden. Zone 7.

H.raoulii var. *pentasepala*

(Latin — penta = five) A more compact and more erect form found along the Upper Awatere Valley and the Hodder River, South Marlborough, South Island, NZ. Grows up to 8 in (20 cm). The leaves are dark green, slightly red edged, not so toothed; length ⅖–¾ in (1–2 cm). Branching spikes of white flowers appear in late April and May, preceded by pink buds.

A plant for the alpine enthusiast. Zone 7.

H.recurva

The leaves of this shrub are spreading and deflexed or curved backwards (from Latin — recurva). *H.recurva* grows in rocky places along streams and the River Aorere in NW Nelson, South Island, NZ. An interesting, compact, free flowering shrub, much branching, spreading and neat, growing up to 36 in (90 cm). The branchlets are sparsely hairy, light brown becoming red brown later. The leaves are glaucous or bluey green and deflexed. The leaf blade is narrow lanceolate, 1–2 in (2.5–5 cm) long and ¼ in (6 mm) wide. 2½ in (6.5 cm) spikes of white flowers appear towards the end of the branchlets, in summer.

A neat, free flowering shrub for the smaller garden, it likes a sunny position and well drained soil. Its neat habit means little pruning. Zone 8.

H.recurva 'Aoira'

The earliest record of *H.recurva* 'Aoira' was in 1923, when the plant was described as a species from Mt. Aoira, NZ in the catalogue of Aldenham Gardens (Hertfordshire ?). Since its return from Kew to Christchurch Botanic Gardens in 1962, it has been found that Mt. Aoira never existed and the only differences between *H.recurva* and *H.*'Aoira' were that the branchlets of *H.*'Aoira' were pubescent all round and not in two bands (bifarious) and it flowered about a fortnight later. So here was an unalterable name and a corruption of Aorere, the river near where *H.recurva* was found. It was decided to make 'Aoira' a cultivar of *H.recurva*. The branchlets are green with a browny green ring at the nodes. The leaves are green and covered with a fine down making them look grey.

For other details, see *H.recurva*. In Maori 'Aorere' means the white torrent and this aptly describes this shrub in flower. Zone 8.

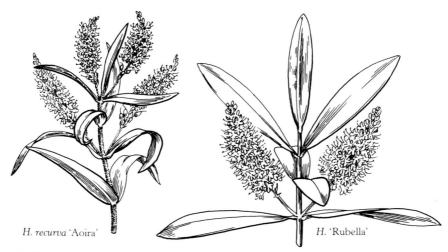

H. recurva 'Aoira'   H. 'Rubella'

8.12 H.recurva *'Aoira'*, H.*'Rubella'*

H.'Red Hugh'

H.'Red Emperor' and *H.*'Pellini's Red' are other names for this attractive cultivar whose origin has not been traced.

A strong growing, compact, upright shrub, growing to 54 in (137 cm) in height. Its reddish brown branchlets, suggest that *H.speciosa* has a part somewhere in the parentage, hence its more tender nature. The leaves are rather convex, up to 2½ in (6.5 cm) in length and 1 in (2.5 cm) wide, with a reddish brown midrib on the underside of the leaf, which is also paler green; the leaf blade is obovate. Growth buds are reddish brown, which can spread to other leaves near the ends of the stems, at times. Strawberry red flowers are packed into spikes, 1½–2 in (4–5 cm) long carried on ½ in (1.25 cm) stalks, in summer.

A good cultivar for the warmer, coastal or sheltered garden, but not hardy everywhere. Zone 10.

H.'Red Ruth'

A synonym of *H.*'Eveline', which see for the description.

H.rigidula

(Latin — rigidus = rigid or stiff) The name refers to the appearance of this shrub, which is found amongst rocks beside streams and along the Pelorus River in Marlborough, South Island, NZ.

An erect, much branched shrub growing from 6–12 in (15–30 cm). The branchlets are yellow green. The leaves are elliptic oblong with thickened edges, glossy green above, duller below; length ½–1 in (1.25–2.5 cm); width about ¼ in (6–8 mm). The leaves are upright then spreading. The leaf bud has a narrow sinus. Spikes of closely arranged white flowers are carried in the tips of the stems in summer.

Another floriferous shrub for the garden as this neat shrub is covered in flowers, when established. It spreads a little wider than the height it grows. Zone 7.

H.'Royal Purple'

Another name for *H.*'Alicia Amherst', which see for description.

H.'Rubella'

A *H.speciosa* hybrid that comes from Aberystwyth in Wales with striking crimson flowers, which contrast well with the dark green foliage.

A fairly compact growing shrub, to a height of 54 in (137 cm), with reddish brown stems and growth buds. The leaves are elliptic ovate, slightly down turning at the margins, dark green, paler on the underside where the midribs are reddish brown. The leaf blade is 2½ in (6.5 cm) long and 1 in (1.25 cm) wide. Crimson flowers, closely arranged on spikes 2 in (5 cm) long, are carried on ¾ in (2 cm) stalks, in summer.

One of the best *H.speciosa* cultivars, as far as flower colour is concerned. It is half hardy. Zone 10.

H.rupicola

(Latin — rupicola = growing in rocky places) and that is where you will find this shrub, in the gorge of the Conway River and other rocky places on the mountains up to 2,000 feet (610 m), from South Marlborough to North Canterbury, South Island, NZ.

An erect branching shrub, growing to about 42 in (105 cm) in height. The branchlets are pubescent, darkish brown. The leaves are elliptic or obovate oblong, yellowish green, green beneath and spreading. The leaf blade is ½–1 in (1.25–2.5 cm) in length by ¼ in (6 mm) wide. White flowers are found just below the tips of the branches, in summer.

Not widely cultivated in gardens; could make a back of border shrub or foil. Zone 8.

H.salicifolia

As the name says, this willow leaved Hebe can be found all over the South and Stewart Islands, although not along the coasts of the Marlborough Sound, from the shoreline to 3,000 ft (915 m). *H.salicifolia* is also found in Chile on the same latitudes (44–45°S).

Much branched, erect to spreading, with branchlets light green with thin brown nodal rings. Grows to a height of 60 in (150 cm), but in less exposed areas can be much more. The leaves are narrow, long lanceolate, up to 5 in (12.5 cm) in length, but only up to ½ in (1.25 cm) in width, noticeably narrowing to the tips. The leaf blades are glossy, mid green, ascending at first, to spreading, with tips tending to down turn; under surface slightly paler. The spike of white flowers often exceeds the length of the leaves and is carried on a 1 in (2.5 cm) stalk, in summer. Some forms can have violet toned flowers which soon fade to white or the spikes can be drooping.

An attractive shrub especially the forms with drooping spikes of flowers. A shrub for screening in coastal or inland areas, or as a graceful shrub for the back of the border. If it tends to grow too tall or wide for the position, prune after flowering. Zone 7, or even Zone 6.

H.salicornioides

The meaning of 'salicornioides' is like a salicornia or Glasswort from the salt marshes (sal = salt, cornu = horn, referring to the horn like branches). *H.salicornioides* is usually found in subalpine scrub in the Nelson, Marlborough and North Canterbury Mts, South Island, NZ, where it tends to be localised. The branchlets all grow erect making it distinct.

A much branched, spreading, whipcord type shrub, growing to a height of 24 in (60 cm) or more. The branches are stout, rather erect with old leaf scars; the branchlets tend to be crowded and are dull yellow green. The leaves are very small, pressed to the stems, joined at the base to form almost a tube for half their length, which is $\frac{1}{16}$ in (1.5 mm). Colour bright green to yellow green, matt not shiny, but fleshy. White flowers are packed into short spikes of up to 12 flowers at the ends of the stems, in early summer.

This Hebe forms mat like growth, so is ideal for ground covering and for growing in rock gardens or along the front of the border. Zone 7.

H.'Sapphire'

It has not been traced where this cultivar came from, but in its parentage is *H.speciosa*, as evidenced by the leaves.

Upright growing, not spreading, well branched and rounded, growing to a height of 54 in (135 cm). The branchlets are light brown with darker brown nodes. The leaves are narrow, elliptic oblong and some are obovate oblong up to $2\frac{1}{2}$ in (6.5 cm) in length and $\frac{2}{5}$ in (1 cm) in width. The leaf blade is dark green in colour with bronze or reddish midribs on both surfaces. At times the reddish colour suffuses over the young leaves and sometimes older leaf upper surfaces in winter. $2\frac{1}{2}$– $3\frac{1}{2}$ in (6.5–9 cm) spikes of rosy purple flowers appear in summer and autumn, and blend with the leaves.

Give some protection, such as planting amongst other shrubs, for which this cultivar is well suited. Zone 9, except in exposed positions.

H.'Simon Delaux'

The origin of this *H.speciosa* cultivar is not known but is possibly French. One of the better *H.speciosa* cultivars.

A much branched rounded shrub, 48 in (120 cm) or more in height. The branchlets are reddish brown. The leaves are dark green, paler beneath, with young leaves suffused plum colour on both surfaces. The leaf bud and the midrib on the under surface are also reddish brown. The leaf blade is obovate or ovate, 2 in (5 cm) long and up to 1 in (2.5 cm) in width. The crimson flowers appear in late summer and autumn and are displayed on spikes at least 4 in (10 cm) in length.

A very good shrub for flower and foliage, but is only for the warmer garden, as it is not hardy. Zone 10.

H.speciosa

This species is confined to sea facing cliffs south of Hokianga Head and Maunganui Bluff in the north and east, Tongapurutu and Urenui in N. Taranaki on the west coast of North Island and at Titirangi Bay in Marlborough Sounds, South Island, NZ.

A rounded, bushy, well branched shrub with stout, smooth, green branchlets, growing to a height of 54 in (135 cm). It has been observed that the two types of leaves, elliptic or obovate, to be found on bushes of *H.speciosa* can usually be found on the bushes of *H.speciosa* hybrids and cultivars from these hybrids. In *H.speciosa* the leaf blade is broad elliptic or obovate oblong, 2–4 in (5–10 cm) long by 1–1¾ in (2.5–4.5 cm) wide. The leaves are dark green, glossy, leathery to rather fleshy and paler below. The leaf stems are short and also rather fleshy. The beetroot purple flowers are closely packed in spikes the length of the leaves, but can vary; the spikes are usually 1½ in (4 cm) across. The flowers tend to be produced over many months of summer and autumn. This is a tender shrub for coastal districts protected from cold winds and frosts. *H.speciosa* has produced many fine hybrids, but all carry this lack of hardiness. Zone 10.

H.'Spender's Seedling'

Its origin and parentage have still to be verified; one parent is possibly *H.parviflora*.

A much branched, slender stemmed, narrow leaved, rounded shrub. The branchlets are browny green with brown nodes, arising at an angle of 45° from the branch. Grows to a height of 24–30 in (60–75 cm), with about a similar spread. The leaves are narrow lanceolate and some have a tendency to be sickle shaped, but all are spreading and down turning. The leaf blade is up to 2½ in (6.5 cm) in length and ⅕ in (5 mm) in width. The colour is bright green, dulling later. Fragrant, white flowers are carried on slender racemes or spikes up to 4 in (10 cm) in length, in summer.

This is an attractive, free flowering cultivar, popular with gardeners. *H.* 'C.P.Raffill' is taller and similar. Zone 9.

H.stricta

As in the South Island one finds *H.salicifolia*, so in the North Island one finds *H.stricta*, which can be distinguished easily, as it has no leaf bud sinus, whereas *H.salicifolia* has. *Hebe stricta* is common in the country and hills north of the Manuwatu River (Palmerston North) in North Island, NZ. It is hardy in most of lowland NZ, but not in Britain away from the south and south west.

A well branched, spreading shrub with yellow green branchlets growing to a height of up to 72 in (180 cm). The leaves are spreading 2–5 in (5–

12.5 cm) long and ⅗–1 in (1.5–2.5 cm) wide, green in colour, paler
beneath. The leaf blade is lanceolate to linear lanceolate, evenly narrowed
at both ends. White or pale bluish white flowers are carried in spikes 3–
6 in (7.5–15 cm) long, usually longer than the leaf, in summer.

A coastal or warmer garden shrub worth growing in the back of the
border, but inland use *H.salicifolia.* Zone 9.

H.stricta var. *egmontiana*

Differs from *H.stricta* in being a compact shrub, rounded in outline and
found only on Mt. Taranaki (Egmont), North Island, NZ. Other details are
the same as *H.stricta.* Zone 9.

H.stricta var *macroura*

From the coastal cliffs of Bay of Plenty and Waikato River southward on
North Island. The main difference from *H.stricta* is the broader, thicker
leaf. The leaves are obovate oblong, up to 3 in (7.5 cm) in length and up to
1¼ in (3 cm) in width. The leaf colour is mid to dark green, the midrib
and margin are lighter and the lower surface is duller and paler. The leaf
blade tends to be thick and stiffly spreading. Other details are as *H.stricta.*
Zone 9.

H. strictissima   *H. stricta var. macroura*

8.13 H.strictissima, H.stricta *var.* macroura

H.stricta vars.

There are two other varieties of *H.stricta*, namely *H.*'Atkinsonii', an openly
branched and heavily wooded shrub, and *H.*'Lata', a compact lower
growing shrub. Both are not widely known or cultivated.

H.strictissima

From Banks Peninsula on the east coast of South Island, NZ. Strictissima comes from the Latin — strictus = straight or erect, and this refers to the habit of this shrub which is very erect. The branchlets, too, tend to be stiff as well as greeny brown with slightly darker nodes. They can be reddish at times. This species is not to be confused with *H.stricta*. The leaves are light to mid green in colour, matt, narrow oblong, ¾–1¾ in (2–4.5 cm) in length, ¼ in (6 mm) in width. The leaf blade narrows towards the tip and is slightly concave. The leaves ascend at first, then gradually spread. The white flowers appear towards the ends of the branchlets in summer. They are closely arranged in long spikes 5 in (12.5 cm) long, ½ in (1.25 cm) wide, carried on 1 in (2.54 cm) stalks.

An interesting shrub growing slowly to a height of 42–48 in (105–120 cm) with a floral display to surprise. It was formerly included with *H*.'Leiophylla'. Zone 9.

H.subalpina

This species grows on the higher rainfall or western sides of the Westland and Canterbury Mountains, South Island, NZ and is to be found at an altitude of 750–1,200 ft (228–365 m) and can be found up to 2,500 ft (762 m) or higher. The name is self explanatory and reflects the area where it grows. This species has been called *H.montana* and, in Britain, *H.rakaiensis* was at one time called *H.subalpina*.

A much branched shrub, rounded in outline, with branchlets green to purple in colour, fairly stout and growing to 42 in (105 cm), sometimes more. The apple green leaves are lanceolate to narrow elliptic, spreading and up to 1 in (2.5 cm) in length and ¼ in (6 mm) wide. The leaf blade is more glossy on the upper surface. The leaf bud is without a sinus. Crowded white flowers appear in spikes 1–1½ in (2.5–4 cm) or more in length, near the ends of the branchlets, in May. A free flowering shrub.

Very hardy shrub for the garden. It can be pruned after flowering to keep it within bounds. Zone 7.

H.subsimilis

The name, 'subsimilis' means nearly similar and refers to the likeness to the related species *H.coarctata*, which is more spreading and taller. *H.subsimilis* belongs to the whipcord group and is found in subalpine scrub and tussock grass along the Ruahine and Tararua Ranges, North Island, NZ. A bushy, densely branched shrub. The branches are upright to spreading and branched at the tips. Grows only to about 10 in (25 cm). The leaves are deltoid, joined at the base for one-third of their length, which is ¹⁄₁₆ in (1.3 mm). The leaf blade is thick and green in colour. White flowers appear in small spikes in late spring. Flowers are not freely produced.

Although a shy flowerer, it is worth growing in rock gardens or troughs, for its whipcord foliage. Zone 7.

H.subsimilis var. *astonii*

Named after the NZ botanist and agrochemist, B.C. Aston, again small growing and yellow green which distinguishes it from *H.subsimilis*. Another shy flowerer.

H.'Subulata' (IS)

Subula is the Latin name for an awl and this refers to the shape of the leaves of this small, yellow green whipcord collected by Owen Fletcher from the summit of the Old Man Range in Otago, South Island, NZ. It has yet to flower and so remains an uncertain species. Of interest more to the botanist than the gardener.

H.(albicans) 'Sussex Carpet'

Mentioned here because it is often written *H.*'Sussex Carpet' and is *H.albicans* 'Prostrate Form'. The name has as yet not been validated. See *H.albicans* 'Prostrate Form' for fuller details of this shrub.

H.tetragona

A shrub with four-angled branches, which is the Latin meaning of tetragona. This species is found in scrub and tussock grassland in the mountain region of Hikurangi, Tongariro and the NW Ruahine Range, North Island, NZ.

A small, much branched shrub, which grows about 24–30 in (60–75 cm) in height. The branches are upright, fairly stout and four-angled. The branchlets are yellow green in colour. Typical of a whipcord, the leaves are small, deltoid, thick, and keeled on the back, smooth and shining, pressed to the stem in opposite pairs to give the four ranks. The leaves are green or yellow green, up to $1/10$ in (2 mm) in length. The flowers appear in a terminal spike of about 12 flowers, white in colour or can be mauve ageing to white, in early summer.

This whipcord is slow growing so ideal for rock garden or front of border, as it is often half the height in cultivation. To help in identifying this species, the leaves have a hairy margin around each leaf. *H.tetragona* has been in Britain since 1839 when J.C. Bidwill sent specimens to Kew from New Zealand. Zone 7.

H.tetrasticha

This species is mentioned because it has separate male and female plants. This is a small shrub, from the mountains of Canterbury, South Island, NZ. The Latin meaning of tetrastichus is four-cornered or four-sided and refers to the branches of this whipcord.

A twiggy shrub growing to about 8 in (20 cm) tall. The branchlets are yellow green. The leaves are very small, deltoid, pressed against the stems and four-ranked. The leaf blade is about $1/12$ in (1.5 mm) long. 1–3 pairs of white flowers appear just below the growing bud on the branchlet. A reluctant flowerer.

A hardy plant for the alpine enthusiast. Zone 7.

H.topiaria

The Roman ornamental gardening of the first century AD was known as ars topiaria and included the clipping of box and other shrubs into shapes of letters and animals, what is known today as topiary. This Hebe also has the 'just clipped' look, hence its Latin name is very appropriate. This shrub is to be found in the mountains of Nelson and the Mt. Arthur tableland, South Island, NZ.

A trim, rounded, well branched shrub, to a height of 36–42 in (90–105 cm). The leaf bud is without a sinus and the leaves are almost overlapping at the end of the branchlets. The leaves are mid green, tending to be fleshy and upward growing. The leaf blade is broadly elliptic to obovate, slightly shiny; length ½ in (1.25 cm); width ¼ in (6 mm). White flowers find their way between the leaves in summer. The flowers are just longer than the leaves at the ends of the branchlets.

This shrub can be used in formal plantings, as well as a specimen shrub or in the shrub border. It needs to be better known in Britain and will reward the gardener who plants it. Zone 8.

H.townsonii

An easily recognisable species, because of a row of short oblique dashes or domatia just within the margin on each side of the underside of the leaf blade. Grows on Mt. Messenger in Taranaki, North Island and near Westport, South Island, NZ, where William Townson (1850–1926) was a pharmaceutical chemist and after whom the shrub is named.

A branched, upright growing shrub, to a height of 42 in (105 cm). The branchlets are yellow green. The leaves are bright green, duller beneath, linear lanceolate, tending to grow upright as well as spreading. The leaf blade is up to 1½ in (4 cm) in length and ¼ in (6 mm) wide. The leaf bud has a sinus. The flowers are white or with a hint of mauve as they open. The racemes of loosely displayed flowers are about 2 in (5 cm) long, and highlight the flowering of this shrub.

A hardy shrub thriving in sun or not too dense shade. A spring flowering shrub for the border. Zone 8.

H.traversii

Henry H. Travers, after whom this Hebe is named, worked on the *Chatham Island Flora*. This Hebe grows on banks and streamsides from Marlborough to mid Canterbury, South Island, NZ.

A loosely branched shrub, to a height of 48 in (120 cm) with slender branchlets arising at the ends of the branches. The branchlets are green in colour becoming brown later. The leaves are dull, yellowish green up to 1 in (2.5 cm) long and ¼ in (6 mm) wide. The leaf blade is narrow oblong. White flowers on short spikes, 1 in (2.5 cm) long, with ½ in (1.25 cm) stalks, appear at the ends of the branchlets, in summer.

A useful space filler for the middle and back of the shrub border. Zone 7.

H.treadwellii

Previously an uncertain species (IS), but now recognised as a species (1987). Named after C.H. Treadwell, a horticulturist from Wellington, North Island, this small, carpeting plant comes from Mt. Oliver in the Sealey Range as well as Cragieburn Range and some other places in South Island, NZ. It can be found at an altitude of 3,600 ft (1,036 m).

The branches are erect and growing up to 6 in (15 cm). The leaves are obovate rounded, small, spreading, four-ranked and dull mid green in colour and paler below; length $^3/_{10}$ in (8 mm); width $^2/_{10}$ in (5 mm). The flowers are displayed in few flowered racemes of two pairs of flowers, almost hidden by leaves, towards the ends of the green branchlets in early summer.

A carpeting plant for the rock garden. Zone 7.

H.'Trixie'

A green leaved seedling from *H.albicans* which arose at County Park Nursery, Essex. Grows to about 15 in (37 cm) in height and spreads to the same width or more across.

This differs from *H.albicans* in having more closely packed leaves on the branchlets, which are green with brown nodes and arise at the ends of the branches. The leaves are mid green, dull with yellow margins. The leaves are slightly concave and arise upward, but have a tendency to down turn towards the end of the blade, which is ovate or ovate oblong; length 1 in (2.5 cm); width $^2/_5$ in (1 cm). Cylindrical spikes of white flowers, $^3/_4$ in (2 cm) long, are carried on fairly long stalks, in summer.

A Hebe for the front of the border or for the larger rock garden. Quite floriferous. Zone 8.

H.truncatula

(Latin — truncatula = ended abruptly or truncated; refers to this shrub's eventual appearance, which is flat topped) This shrub is found on the edges of the forests on the Ruahine Mountains, North Island, NZ

Many branched from ground level, with the branchlets minutely hairy. Grows up to 60 in (150 cm). The leaves are dull green to glossy, paler below, spreading with a tendency to upturn. The leaf blade is elliptic oblong, about 1¼ in (3 cm) in length and ¼ in (6 mm) wide. Few white flowers appear on slender spikes, in summer.

The cultivation of this species in gardens is doubtful. Zone 8.

H.urvilleana

From D'Urville Island off the north coast of the South Island, NZ in the Cook Strait. Both the Island and the plants take their names from Jules Sebastian Cesar, Dumont d'Urville (1790–1844), a French naval officer and author of a *Falkland Islands Flora*.

A rather laxly branched shrub with slender branchlets which are very finely pubescent; as they age they become smooth and grey. The yellow green leaves are up to 1 in (2.5 cm) in length, narrow oblong in shape, narrowed abruptly to the tips. There are minute hairs along the margins and at the base of the leaves. White flowers appear near the ends of the branchlets, in summer.

A coastal shrub with limited potential for the garden. Zone 9.

H.'Veitchii'

Another name for H.'Alicia Amherst' which see for description.

H.venustula

In Latin, venustula means lovely or beautiful and it is that, when this shrub is in full flower. A rounded shrub from the mountains of Hikurangi to the Volcanic Plateau and Cape Palliser, North Island, NZ, found at over 2,500 ft (762 m) in the subalpine scrub. H.'Laevis' and H.'Azunea' or H.'Azurea' are said to be the same as H.venustula. Collenso collected H.'Laevis' and R. Hill collected H.'Azunea' in the Ruahine Mountains, North Island.

A bushy shrub, globular in shape, growing to a height of 42 in (105 cm). The branchlets are yellow green. The leaves are bright green, elliptic oblong, dull beneath about ½ in (1.25 cm) in length and ¼ in (6 mm) in width. One or two branchlets of white flowers appear towards the ends of the stems, in early summer.

A hardy floriferous shrub for the garden, especially the shrub border. Zone 7.

H.vernicosa

(Latin — vernicosus = shiny or varnished; refers to the leaves). This shrub grows on the floors of beech forests from the shore to the tree line in Marlborough, East Nelson and the West Amuri district, South Island, NZ.

A well branched, semi erect shrub, making a globular shaped bush, about 15 in (37 cm) in height. The branchlets are greeny brown, with brown nodes. The leaves are dark, lustrous green, concave and upright at first, flattening and spreading later. The leaf blade is ⅖ in (1 cm) long and ⅕ in (5 mm) wide. The flowers are white or lavender soon fading to white, and are held in short spikes, up to 1–1½ in (2.5–4 cm), in pairs, in the leaf axils behind the growing bud, in late spring.

An attractive species for the smaller garden. Once established it is a free flowerer, ideal for rock gardens. Zone 7.

H.'Violet Meikle'

A bushy shrub raised in Auckland, North Island, NZ and named after the Nurseryman's wife, Mrs Violet Meikle. A distinct cultivar with leaves and habit like H.speciosa but the flowers are more like H.elliptica (NZ).

A much branched shrub growing to about 48 in (120 cm). The branchlets are green and erect, suffused purple. The young leaves are suffused purple; older leaves are green with a dull gloss, paler beneath. The leaf blade is oblanceolate to oblong ovate, 2½–3 in (6.5–7.5 cm) long. Dark purple flowers crowd spikes a little longer than the leaves, arising at the tips of the branchlets, in summer. This is the feature of this half hardy shrub.

Sheltered, warmer gardens for this distinct and colourful, but tender, cultivar. Zone 10.

H.'Violet Snow'

A *H.salicifolia* hybrid that arose in Mr Michael Haworth-Booth's, Far All Nursery in Hampshire.

A fairly upright, much branched shrub growing to about 54 in (135 cm). The branchlets are green with brown nodes. The pale green leaves are slightly shiny, narrowing to the tip, paler beneath. The leaf blade is lanceolate and spreading. White tipped violet flowers are carried in spikes about the length of the leaves. Summer flowering.

With its large leaves, length 4–4½ in (10–11.5 cm); width ¾–1 in (2–2.5 cm), it can suffer wind chill damage in exposed sites. It is not quite so hardy as its parent, *H.salicifolia*. However, if damaged, it is a quick growing shrub. Zone 9.

H.'Violet Wand'

Possibly the tallest growing member of the 'Wand' group of hybrids raised by Treseders of Truro, Cornwall from *H.*'Miss. E. Fittall' and can grow to 72 in (180 cm).

Upright growing, well branched, but not too spreading. The branchlets

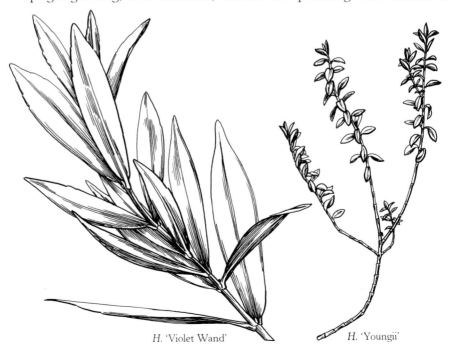

H. 'Violet Wand'   H. 'Youngii'

8.14 H.'Violet Wand' of the 'Wand Group', and ground covering H.'Youngii' are green then browny green with darker nodes later. The leaves are oblong lanceolate, narrowing more to the tip, mid green but paler below; length 4–4½ in (10–11.5 cm) and width ⅘–1 in (2–2.5 cm). The leaves are spreading. Eye catching spikes of violet and white flowers, sometimes up to 9 in (22.5 cm) in length, appear in summer.

An ideal back of the border shrub, especially in coastal districts or where influenced by the coastal climate. Zone 9.

H.'Waikiki'

Although named after the famous Honolulu Beach, nothing more is known as to where this cultivar was raised.

An upright, not too spreading bush, growing to a height of 48 in (120 cm). The branchlets are green with a brown nodal ring. The leaves are mid green, ovate elliptic, slightly shiny, but paler beneath. The leaf blade is 1–1½ in (2.5–4 cm) in length and up to ½ in (1.25 cm) wide. In winter the young leaves at the ends of the branchlets become coppery red. The bluey mauve flowers, in medium length spikes about twice the length of the leaves, appear early to midsummer.

A useful back of the border shrub because of its winter foliage, which is also of interest to flower arrangers. Can also be used as a hedging shrub. Zone 9.

H.'Walter Buccleugh'

A H.'Youngii' seedling from Boughton, Northants, similar to H.'Colwall' in habit of growth.

A spreading, low growing shrub, with decumbent branches. The branchlets are reddish green, so too are the growth buds; the colouring is more marked in winter. The leaves are green, slightly concave, paler below. The leaf blade is ovate, ²/₁₀ in (5 mm) long and ¹/₁₀ in (2 mm) wide. Light purple flowers are carried in short spikes, with reddish brown stems, in summer.

A shrub for the rock garden. Zone 8.

H.'Wardiensis'

The origin of this rock plant is not known: with the Latin ending to the name it suggests a place not a person.

A much branching, small growing plant to about 8 in (20 cm) in height. The fairly erect branchlets are green in colour with brown nodes. The leaves are oval to elliptic, small, up to ½ in (1.25 cm) in length and ²/₁₀ in (5 mm) in width. The leaf blade is flat, with a tendency to down turn, grey green in colour, rather widely spaced and stiff. Terminal clusters of white flowers appear at the ends of the branchlets, in summer.

A useful plant for the rock garden. Zone 8.

H.'Warleyensis'

Occasionally called H.'Warley', referring to Warley Place, the home and garden of Miss Ellen Willmott (1858–1954).

A neat, dwarf shrub, with distinctive dark brown stems. It grows to about 30 in (75 cm) in height. The leaves are obovate, narrowing towards the stem, 1½ in (4 cm) long, ⅖ in (1 cm) wide. Deep green and glossy, they tend to be upright at first, then spreading. The same dark reddish brown colour of the stems appears in a paler form on the midribs on the under surface of the leaves, as well as on the under surface of the leaves around the buds at the ends of the stems. Methyl violet in colour, the flowers are carried in pointed spikes up to 2 in (5 cm) in length. The stalk is about ¾ in (2 cm) in length, then a pair of small leaves and often a pair of secondary flower spikes. There can often be as many as four pairs of primary flower spikes below the growing bud. Summer flowering and into autumn as well.

A useful foliage and flowering shrub for the border. Fairly hardy away from piercing cold easterly winds. Zone 9.

H.'Warley Pink'

Named after Warley Place in Essex (see H.'Warleyensis'). This is a H.*speciosa* cultivar forming a rounded shrub.

An upright, well branched shrub growing to a height of 60 in (150 cm). The branchlets are green. The leaves appear stiff and erect at first but gradually spread till at right angles to the stem. The leaf blade is elliptic up to 3 in (7.5 cm) long and 1 in (2.5 cm) wide. Mid green in colour, shiny, lighter below. Pink flowers, with deeper pink centres, appear on 3 in (7.5 cm) spikes with 1 in (2.5 cm) stalks, in summer.

A half hardy shrub for the warmer garden. Zone 10.

H.'Watson's Pink'

A cultivar of the H.'Carnea' group, raised at Watson's Nursery, Killiney, Eire.

A neat upright growing shrub, with greeny brown branchlets, with darker brown nodes; height 42 in (105 cm). The leaves are narrow oblong elliptic up to 2 in (5 cm) in length and ⅖ in (1 cm) in width. The leaf blade is mid green. Bright pink flowers are attractively displayed in summer on spikes about the same length as the leaves.

A very good shrub, where it can be grown, in the shrub border. Zone 9, or even Zone 10.

H.'Wendy'

A seedling from H.'Youngii', fairly free flowering, raised at County Park Nursery, Essex. A carpeting plant with short, sometimes branching, racemes of well spaced flowers, white in colour tinged with blue in May and June. The leaves are pale green, about ⅖ in (1 cm) long. A rock garden plant growing to 4 in (10 cm) in height. Zone 8.

H.'White Heather'

The origin of this dubiously named plant has been given as London, but that is not certain. According to the rules, a plant should not be named after or given the name of another plant.

More or less upright growing but at the same time much branched and spreading, rounded in outline and up to 15 in (37 cm) in height. The branchlets are browny green with brown nodes. The dark green leaves are variable in length up the stem. The leaf shape is ovate oblong and the leaf blade is $3/4$–$1\frac{1}{2}$ in (2–4 cm) in length and $2/10$–$4/10$ in (5–10 mm) wide. White flowers are carried on spikes $2\frac{1}{2}$–3 in (6.5–7.5 cm) long, with $3/4$–1 in (2–2.5 cm) stalk, which arise in leaf axils slightly below the ends of the branchlets in early summer and at other times.

A good cultivar for the mixed borders, as its dark green leaves arranged in four ranks at right angles to the stem, make a good foil for other plants. Zone 9.

H.'White Wand'

One of the hardiest members of the 'Wand' group, raised by Treseders of Truro, Cornwall and growing up to 60 in (150 cm).

Fairly upright, much branched, yet round, but not too spreading. The branchlets are yellow green with brown nodes. The leaves are yellow green, slightly shiny, spreading and slightly down turning. The leaf blade is oblong lanceolate, up to $3\frac{1}{2}$ in (9 cm) long and $3/4$ in (2 cm) wide. The very long spikes of white flowers are up to 7 in (18 cm) in length by $3/4$ in (2 cm) in width. Summer and autumn flowering.

A very useful back of the border shrub. Zone 9.

H.'Willcoxii'

D. Petrie recorded H.'Willcoxii' in 1911 as coming from Routeburn Valley, Lake Wakitipu, South Island, NZ, but it has never been recognised.

A neat, small, branched shrub growing to about 6 in (15 cm). It is slow growing with greeny brown branchlets. The leaves are four-ranked, at right angles to the stem. The leaf blade is rounded elliptic, with a lighter margin, finely pubescent on both surfaces, slightly concave, green in colour; length $1/5$ in (5 mm); width about $1/10$ in (2 mm). Crowded small spikes of white flowers appear at the ends of the branches, in summer.

An excellent plant for troughs or rock gardens. Zone 7.

H.'Wine Red'

A H.speciosa cultivar, which was collected in Guernsey and possibly raised there. Grows to 54 in (137 cm) tall. Nicely coloured shrub for warmer garden.

Fairly upright, yet rounded and well branched with reddish brown stems. The leaves are elliptic ovate, 2–$2\frac{1}{2}$ in (5–6.5 cm) in length and up to 1 in (2.5 cm) in width. Mid-dark green, glossy, paler on the underside and tending to grow upward. The under surfaces of the young leaves around the buds at the end of the stem, the bud itself and the midribs of the older leaves are reddish brown in colour. The name 'Wine Red' aptly describes the flower colour, which is pinky purple. The flowers are carried on 3 in (7.5 cm) spikes in mid to late summer. Zone 10.

H.'Wingletye'

A seedling from *H.pimeleoides* var. *glaucocaerulea*, named after the lane which leads to County Park Nursery, Essex.

A prostrate, spreading, grey foliaged Hebe, to a height of 6 in (15 cm), with horizontal brown stems and leaves that tend to flatten in one plane. The leaves are glaucous, obovate, ⅖ in (1 cm) in length and ⅕ in (5 mm) in width, and tend to spread. Amethyst flowers on 1 in (2.5 cm) spikes, are carried clear of the leaves by ½ in (1.25 cm) stalks towards the ends of the stems, in early summer.

A very good rock garden or trough plant. Zone 8.

H.'Winter Glow'

A stronger growing plant than the parent *H.*'Youngii' raised at County Park Nursery, Essex. Differs from the parent also in having oval, green, concave leaves that are slightly glaucous, but becoming reddish in winter. The leaves are ½ in (1.25 cm) in length and ¼ in (6 mm) in width. Blue flowers on branching racemes appear in June and July. Zone 8.

H.'Youngii'

This popular cultivar arose as a chance cross between *H.elliptica* and *H.pimeleoides* in Christchurch Botanic Gardens, South Island, NZ, and was named after James Young, a past Curator of the Botanic Gardens. *H.*'Youngii' is the validated name. When Mr Carl Teschner, a Nurseryman of Otago, South Island sent an unnamed cultivar to Miss Valerie Finnis in England, she named it after the sender. Later the plant was exhibited at the Royal Horticultural Society where it received an Award of Merit as *H.*'Carl Teschner'. This cultivar has since been checked against the original *H.*'Youngii' and has been found to be identical. In Britain, where we were reluctant to use Hebe instead of Veronica, we should now use the older, validated name of *H.*'Youngii'.

A spreading, decumbent, much branched shrub, not growing more than 9 in (23 cm) in height. The branchlets are dark brown. The leaves are broad obovate, ¼–½ in (6–12 mm) long and ⅕ in (5 mm) wide. The leaf blade is green above and paler below, spreading. Violet flowers in loose racemes, 1½ in (4 cm) long, appear towards the ends of the stems, in summer.

A popular shrub for rock garden, front of borders or troughs. Zone 8.

H.'Youngii Minor'

Previously *H.*'Carl Teschner Minor'. A neater, less spreading form of *H.*'Youngii' and to be used for the same purposes.

9

Chionohebe species

This genus of Chionohebe (family — Scrophulariaceae) arose, in 1985, from what was previously Pygmea, because of their close relationship to Hebe and more so to Parahebe, as the flowers bear some resemblance. The Chionohebes (Greek — chion, pronounced kion = snow) are mainly cushion forming plants from the mountainous regions of New Zealand in Nelson, Marlborough, Canterbury and Otago in South Island. The six species have white flowers and small leaves. All grow close to the snow line, hence are difficult to grow in the normal British climate. Well drained, gritty soils, in exposed positions are preferred to warmer, enclosed gardens. As these plants are a challenge to grow, they are more for the expert or alpine enthusiast.

There are only six species of Chionohebe, the flowers of which are solitary, five-lobed, white in colour and mostly sessile. Two of the species, *C.armstrongii* and *C.densifolia*, are low growing, much branched shrubs. All species are variable in leaf shape, height and spread and the tightness of the cushion or growth. Any measurements are approximate.

Of the six species, the three species most likely to be grown are *C.ciliolata*, *C.densifolia* and *C.pulvinaris*. Only brief descriptions have been given; fuller descriptions can be found in any Flora of New Zealand native plants.

C.armstrongii

A rigid, much branched shrub, with prostrate habit, only ½–1¼ in (1.5–3 cm) in height, with small, ovate, tough, leathery leaves, which are pressed to the stems. The flowers are white and funnel shaped.

C.ciliolata

Dense, hoary, green cushions of varying height and spread. The average height is 1¼ in (3 cm) and spread 4 in (10 cm). The narrow, ovate, thick, leathery leaves have hairs on the leaf margins.

C.densifolia

Previously *P.tetragona*; when it became Chionohebe, its name was changed and misspelt 'densiflora'. A much branched, rather rigid shrub forming mats or patches of loose woody stems, which tend to root. Grows to about 2 in (5 cm) in height, with small, thick, green leaves. The flower buds are sometimes violet, but open to reveal fairly large white flowers.

131

C.myosotoides

Another cushion forming, woody shrub, with obovate to spathulate leaves, which are covered with soft greyish hairs. Similar to *C.pulvinaris*, it has the same leathery leaves and white flowers.

C.pulvinaris

Slender erect branchlets, arising from woody branches, which tightly compact to form a dense hoary, grey green cushion, 1–1½ in (2.5–4 cm) in height and about 5 in (12–13 cm) across. Leaves again small and linear oblong; pressed against the stems.

C.thomsonii

Again similar to *C.pulvinaris*, only forming more rigid cushions. The branchlets are more woody, the leaves are yellow green and glossy underneath, and are pressed against the stems. The leaves are linear spathulate, leathery with fine hairs, except on the margins.

10

Parahebe species, varieties and cultivars

Parahebes are very useful evergreen plants, providing cover in rock gardens and borders. The attractive flowers are veined and in white, pink, blue and purple. *Parahebe catarractae*, the Waterfall Veronica as it was called, is known to gardeners, but there are other species and cultivars worthy of greater use in the garden. There are eleven species of Parahebes, all from New Zealand, although descriptions of four species have not been included, namely: *P.cheesemanii*, *P.plano-petiolata*, *P.spathulata* and *P.trifida*. These species are not easy to grow, being mountain subshrubs, and are more for the alpine house and the expert, as far as Britain is concerned.

The descriptions follow the pattern of the Hebe list: origin, habit of growth, leaf shape and size, flower colour and hardiness. The habits of growth are illustrated in Figure 8.1. As most Parahebes are ground covering, heights to which they grow will only be given where it exceeds 4 in (10 cm).

P.birleyi

The highest growing Parahebe at altitudes of 6,500–9,800 ft (2,000–3,000 m), from Mt. Cook, South Island, NZ, and has yet to come down to cultivation in gardens. A straggling subshrub forming a loose mat, 8 in (20 cm) across. The leaves are fleshy and reddish green, broadly obovate, 3–5 toothed at the tip. White flowers about ³⁄₅ in (15 mm) across, singly usually. Hardy. Zone 7.

P.canescens

This very small species grows along lake sides from the coast to part way up the mountains in Canterbury and Otago, South Island, NZ. Has yet to come into cultivation in the garden. A creeping Parahebe forming small mats, 6–8 in (15–20 cm) across with hairy stems and branches; mid to dark green leaves, with paler under surface; flowers blue and funnel shaped. Zone 8.

P.catarractae

Grows along streamsides, on cliffsides and rocky places on North, South and Stewart Islands, NZ.

A spreading, ground covering subshrub with semi-erect branchlets growing up to 8 in (20 cm). The leaves are lanceolate to elliptic, toothed, mid to dark green, with a paler under surface, variable in size up to 1 in (2.5 cm) long and ¾ in (2 cm) wide. Speedwell or saucer like flowers, veined purple, are displayed in summer in racemes, 1½–4 in (4–10 cm) in length.

An ideal plant for the rock garden or front of the border. Zone 8.

P.catarractae 'Blue Form' and 'White Form'

P.catarractae can be rather a variable plant in the wild and any variations have to be propagated vegetatively and the same is so with any cultivars. *P.catarractae* 'Blue Form' is similar in growth to *P.catarractae*, but has veined deep blue flowers, whereas *P.catarractae* 'White Form' has veined pure white flowers. Both are summer flowering.

P.catarractae 'Delight'

Its origin is unknown, but this has been cultivated in NZ gardens for many years and is becoming known in Britain. The flowers are veined heliotrope in colour. It is better than the species, as the flowers are well coloured and are produced over the summer months in greater abundance. There is a purple ring around the centre of the flowers.

P.catarractae 'Miss Willmott'

The origin was possibly Warley Place Gardens in Essex. Growth like *P.catarractae*, but flowers are veined mauve in colour, in summer.

P.catarractae 'Porlock Purple'

Originated in Dr Hadden's garden at Porlock, Somerset. It is said to be similar to the cultivar *P.catarractae* 'Delight'. The flower is heliotrope with the beetroot purple ring at the base of the petals.

P.decora

Another mountain species from screes, river beds and rocky areas in Hooker Valley and east of the divide in South Island, NZ.

A prostrate subshrub, branched, but rather rigid in appearance and forming variable mats of growth in size and density. The leaves are ovate to rounded, green, sometimes reddish when young and often with two crenations or teeth. The leaf blade is up to ³⁄₁₆ in (4 mm) in length and about ⅛ in (3 mm) in width. The flowers are veined white to pinkish, open bowl shaped, about ⅖ in (1 cm) across.

Another rock garden plant, can be variable. Zone 8.

P.decora 'Gillian'

Said to be a cross between *P.decora* and *P.lyallii* raised by Mr K. Beckett at Stanhoe in Norfolk. The leaves have the two crenations of *P.decora*, an occasional leaf has two pairs of crenations. Older leaves are ³⁄₁₀ in (8 mm) long and ²⁄₁₀ in (5 mm) wide; young leaves are less than ¹⁄₁₀ in (2 mm) long and ¹⁄₂₀ in (1 mm) wide. The leaves are rounded or orbicular, green in colour. The flowers are small, white and carried on slender racemes.

A cultivar for troughs and rock gardens, with its spreading, prostrate growth. Zone 9.

P.decora 'Kea'

(pronounced key-ah) Named after the mischievous alpine parrot of NZ. The rounded mid green leaves have two crenations, which links with P.decora, whereas if this was a hybrid there would be more than two crenations, as is the case with P. 'Bidwillii' (P.decora × P.lyallii).

Prostrate and spreading, a little loose in growth. The leaves are rounded, shiny and displayed on one plane. The leaf blade is ⅕ in (5 mm) in length, ⅛ in (3 mm) in width. Speedwell like, bluey mauve flowers are displayed on slender racemes, in summer.

A cultivar for troughs. Zone 9.

P.decora 'Rose Hybrid'

Similar to the other two cultivars, this has the same two crenations in the leaf and differs in having slightly smaller leaves and the branchlets seem more erect to give a more rounded subshrub. Length of leaf blade is ³⁄₁₆ in (4 mm) and width ⅛ in (3 mm). The leaves are green, rounded ovate, the branchlets brown and the flowers rosy mauve in slender racemes, which appear in summer.

Uses as before. Zone 9.

P.hookeriana

From the subalpine, open rocky places in the mountain ranges of the southern half of North Island, NZ. Not unlike P.catarractae in habit, but with thicker, fleshy leaves. Leaf blade ¼–½ in (6–12 mm) long and ⅛–¼ in (3–6 mm) wide, rounded to ovate in shape, sparsely pubescent and deeply toothed or crenate. The flowers are lavender or white and appear in 4–8 flowered racemes in summer.

A plant for the alpine grower. Zone 9.

P.linifolia

Found in mountain ranges over South Island, NZ from 1,500–5,000 ft (457–1,525 m) and mostly in wet rocky places. A small, well branched subshrub, inclined to sprawl and growing to 6 in (15 cm) in height. The leaves are spreading linear to linear lanceolate, ½–¾ in (1.25–2 cm) long and up to ⅛ in (3 mm) wide. Dark green, shiny but paler beneath. The flowers are saucer shaped, veined, white to pink carried in 1–3 short racemes, four or more flowered, in summer.

A plant for the rock garden. Plant in semi shade. Zone 9.

P.linifolia 'Blue Skies'

A form of P.linifolia collected by Mr L.J. Metcalf on Mt. Owen, South Island, NZ. Similar to P.linifolia in habit of growth and shape of leaves, but the flowers are larger, up to ¾ in (2 cm) across, slightly flatter in shape, lavender colour, with a purple ring in the flower centre. Longer flowering, late spring, midsummer and sometimes later.

An attractive cultivar for the rock garden. Zone 9.

P.lyallii

Subalpine, even lowland, rocky places, common in South Island, NZ. This plant is named in recognition of the work of the botanist, David Lyall (1817–1895), who collected plants in NZ.

A low growing, much branched, subshrub with slender stems, reddish at first, becoming woody later at the base. The leaves are ovate, oblong, slightly toothed, mid to dark green, under surface paler, up to ½ in (1–2 cm) long, or more, and ½ in (1.25 cm) in width. The flowers are white veined pink, saucer shaped, ⅖ in (1 cm) across, displayed on racemes up to 3 in (7 cm) in length, during the summer.

Another useful rock plant. Zone 9.

P.'Mervyn'

Parahebe lyallii could be one of the parents of this hybrid raised by Mr Mervyn Feasey of North Devon. A low growing, spreading subshrub with red edged leaves, which suffuse purple in summer. The flowers are lilac blue and carried in racemes, in summer.

Zone 9.

Parahebe perfoliata comes from Australia and is known as Digger's Speed-well. At the present time it is fitted uneasily into *Parahebe* and could be returned to Veronica or follow Hebe and Parahebe and be given a genus of its own. Until then, details are given below.

Parahebe perfoliata

A dwarf subshrub with slender branches arising from underground stems, erect at first, then falling over and becoming decumbent. These stems can be more than 12 in (30 cm) in length, and grow through the leaves (the meaning of perfoliata). Each pair of glaucous or grey green leaves are joined across the base to make a single leaf and each pair is alternate or at right angles to the pair below. The width of a single leaf is 1½ in (4 cm); the joined leaves are 3 in (8 cm) across. The flowers are violet in colour, Veronica like and loosely placed along the racemes, of which there are a pair at the end of the stem. The racemes are up to 3 in (8 cm) in length of which 1 in (2.5 cm) is stalk. The racemes are erect and droop over from about two-thirds towards the tip. The flowers appear in early summer.

This is an unusual plant for the rockery, small border or large trough in milder areas. The growth can also be deciduous (die down in winter). Zone 9.

Appendix 1

HEBE × 'FRANCISCANA'

Following an article about the Hedging Veronica of the Isles of Scilly, which appeared in the *News* of the Botanical Society of the British Isles, a reader asked: 'Why is it named after San Francisco?' What follows is an example of how important it is to keep records and to have any plant you have raised, registered and the name you wish to give it, accepted and validated by the Registrar for that genus.

To find the connection with San Francisco took many hours of searching, through books, records and articles, and revealed a fascinating story, which will now be given in chronological order, rather than as it was unravelled.

1768–1771

Captain James Cook (1728–1779) in the *Endeavour*, a 368-ton bark (barque) sailed around Cape Horn to the Pacific Ocean to observe the partial eclipsing of the Sun by the planet Venus off the island of Otaheite (Tahiti) in June 1769. Afterwards he sailed south and on 6 October sighted the east coast of the North Island of New Zealand, landing in Poverty Bay near what is now Gisborne. Cook circumnavigated both Islands and charted the coast as he went so efficiently that the charts remained in use for over 150 years.

Botanists Joseph Banks and Daniel Solander were on board and when the ship anchored to refurbish in Ship Cove (Queen Charlotte Sound on the north coast of South Island), they had much time to study the native fauna and flora of the area until the ship left for home in March 1770. Sailing up the east coast of Australia, through Dutch East Indies and around the Cape of Good Hope, they circumnavigated the world.

Dr Solander wrote his 'Primitiae Florae Novae Zelandiae' during the voyage, describing 360 species of plants, and also prepared plates of the plants found at Poverty Bay — where they first landed, Hawke Bay and Queen Charlotte Sound, but the book was never published.

1772–1775

Captain Cook's second voyage to New Zealand and Antarctica, with the botanists and plant collectors J.R. and G. Forster and A. Sparmann on board. After the strenuous voyage to Antarctica, the ship anchored in Dusky Sound on the south west corner of South Island, giving the botanists time to explore the flora, before sailing on to Queen Charlotte Sound and Hawke Bay with time for more plant collecting and exploration.

1776

J.R. and G. Forster described, together with plates, 37 genera and 134 species they had collected on their voyage to New Zealand, and this was published in London in that year. Amongst the plants introduced to Britain was *Veronica elliptica* (Forster), which was to be found later on the west coast of South Island and from Cape Egmont southward on North Island. This shrub was known to the Maoris as the Kokumuka. So here was the first plant in the 'Franciscana' story.

1789

In *Hort. Kewensis*, W. Aiton described *Veronica decussata* (Solander) from the Falkland Islands but he did not say how and when it arrived in Britain, but it could have been prior to 1789. Here then is the second plant.*

1791

J.F. Gmelin described *Veronica magellanica* from southern South America and this plant turned out to be the same plant as W. Aiton had described, namely *Veronica decussata*. W. Aiton had in his article mentioned that *V.decussata* had been found in specimens from southern South America.

1833–1834

K.R. Cunningham (1793–1835) made his expedition to New Zealand and he found, growing on the South Head of Hokianga Harbour, *Veronica speciosa* and thus our third plant was introduced to England in 1835. Details of this expedition and the plants collected were described by his brother, A. Cunningham (1791–1839), in *Companion to Botanical Magazine*, in 1837.

1859–1860

Veronica elliptica (Forster) was crossed with *Veronica speciosa* (A. Cunningham) by a gardener signing himself 'Devonian' and who sent a plant to the Editor of the *Gardeners Chronicle* in 1859. This plant was passed to the Royal Horticultural Society, who distributed 70 plants in 1860 under the name *Veronica decussata*'Devoniana'. No further reference to this plant or as to whom 'Devonian' was, has been discovered. This shrub has spread around the coasts of the south west of England, where it is to be found today. This Veronica also spread to Guernsey, the Isles of Scilly — where it became known as the 'Hedging Veronica'.

1862

Veronica decussata (Solander) was crossed by Isaac Anderson-Henry of Maryfield, Edinburgh with *Veronica speciosa* (A. Cunningham) and a

---

Footnote:

*Lt William Clayton RN, stationed at Port Egmont, West Falkland, 1773–1774, is presumed to have brought seed back with him, and this was grown by Dr John Fothergill in his garden at Stratford, Essex, in about 1776.

number of seedlings were raised. One seedling is preserved in the herbarium at Kew and dated November 1862; with it is another identical seedling dated April 1862. *Veronica*'Lobelioides' was the name given to this cross by its raiser and it was distributed under this name.

1868

Botanist and plant collector, English-born T. Kirk (1828–1898), a writer in New Zealand from 1863, reported the arrival of *Veronica*'Lobelioides' in New Zealand in 1868 from Melbourne, Australia.

1868–1869

Veronica'Blue Gem' was raised prior to 1869 by Mr H.W. Warren, a nurseryman from Salisbury. A brief description was given on p. 1018 in the *Gardeners Chronicle* dated 15 September 1869. On 21 September, Mr Warren showed the plant in London and received a First Class Certificate.

1889

Veronica decussata'Lobelioides' had arrived at Golden Gate Park, San Francisco from Australia and is listed from that date on. By 1913 it was well established in the Park.
Veronica'Lobelioides' was being grown at Kew.

1915

John Fraser, whose herbarium is at Kew, became interested in *Veronica* 'Blue Gem' and obtained specimens of this plant from a variety of sources. To all, he appended the name *Veronica*'Lobelioides' as shown for example on this specimen from Druce; the British horticultural writer and gardener:

Veronica elliptica × *Veronica speciosa*
Veronica 'Lobelioides' Hort. (older name)
Veronica 'Blue Gem' (more recent name)

This hybrid has reached round the seaboard of southern Britain and has been taken to Australia and New Zealand.

1926

Dr L. Cockayne and Dr H.H. Allan submitted a paper on the 'Present Taxonomic Status of the New Zealand Species of Hebe' and this was published in the October by the New Zealand Institute. As a result, their case was accepted for Hebe to become a separate genus and divorced from Veronica.

1943

Miss Alice Eastwood of the Californian Academy of Sciences checked the plants in Golden Gate Park and found the description of *Veronica decussata* did not fit the Veronicas growing there, so she concluded that she had found a new hybrid. Possibly she had the description of *Veronica decussata*'Devoniana' and not *Veronica decussata*'Lobelioides'. This new hybrid was given the name of Hebe × 'Franciscana', after San Francisco, by Miss Eastwood.

1956

Plant material was sent to Kew for identification from the Golden Gate Park, San Francisco. At that time John Souster was working on the genus *Hebe*, still being called *Veronica*, trying to sort out the confusion in the naming of the species. He identified the plant specimens as *Veronica* (*Hebe*) 'Blue Gem'. At that time the names in use for *Veronica* 'Blue Gem' were *Veronica* 'Lobelioides' or *V.decussata* 'Blue Gem' or *V.elliptica* 'Blue Gem'. For brevity Souster decided on validating Hebe × 'Franciscana Blue Gem'. What then was to happen to the other hybrids? *V.decussata* could no longer be used, because *H.* × 'Franciscana' was now the validated name. This name was then applied to the hybrids and *Veronica decussata* 'Devoniana' became *H.* × 'Franciscana', *Veronica decussata* var. *variegata* became *H.* × 'Franciscana Variegata' and *Veronica decussata* 'Lavender Queen' became *H.* × 'Franciscana Lavender Queen'.

The validation of Hebe × 'Franciscana Blue Gem' also confirmed that *V.*'Blue Gem' and *V.*'Lobelioides' were the same and that H.W. Warren and Isaac Anderson-Henry had used the same species, *Veronica* (*Hebe*) *speciosa* and *Veronica elliptica* (Solander, Falkland Islands), to produce this popular hybrid.

1987

When writing this history of *H.* × 'Franciscana' it was discovered that *H.speciosa* had two different shapes of leaf blade on the same shrub, elliptic and obovate, and this characteristic is passed on to the hybrids and the hybrid cultivars. It has since been found that *H.elliptica* (Solander) from the Falkland Islands also has characteristics which it passes onto its hybrids. These features are a rounded apex to the leaf blade, and the leaf stalks (petioles) arise at an angle outward from the node. Both these characteristics are carried in the leaves of *H.* × 'Franciscana 'Blue Gem'.

H.elliptica (Forster) from New Zealand has leaf blades which are pointed at the apex and the leaf stalks arising from the nodes are close to the stem until the leaf blade is reached and this spreads outward. The pointed leaves pass through to the hybrids and are more obvious on the elliptic leaves, whereas the way the leaves arise is present in all hybrids; *H.* × 'Franciscana Lavender Queen', *H.* × 'Franciscana Sarnia' with white flowers and *H.* × 'Franciscana' itself. *H.* × 'Franciscana Variegata' has the leaf stalks close to the stem, but being a branch sport from a stem with obovate leaves, the leaf feature is difficult to find.

Not all may have been discovered about *H.*× 'Franciscana', but what has been discovered so far makes interesting reading. It has not been possible to devote more time to researching this cultivar, with many more cultivars to describe. The possibility of tracing the parentage by the shape of the leaves and the manner in which they attach to the stem is worth considering in future research work, not only with the species responsible for *H.*× 'Franciscana, but maybe with other species and cultivars.

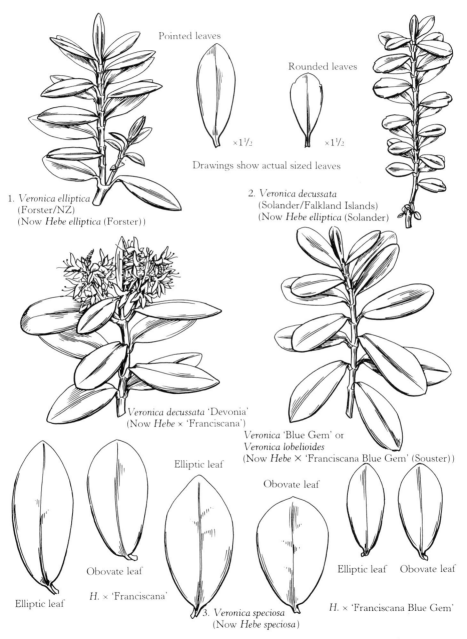

Pointed leaves

Rounded leaves

×1¹/₂

×1¹/₂

Drawings show actual sized leaves

1. *Veronica elliptica*
(Forster/NZ)
(Now *Hebe elliptica* (Forster))

2. *Veronica decussata*
(Solander/Falkland Islands)
(Now *Hebe elliptica* (Solander))

Veronica decussata 'Devonia'
(Now *Hebe* × 'Franciscana')

Veronica 'Blue Gem' or
Veronica lobelioides
(Now *Hebe* × 'Franciscana Blue Gem' (Souster))

Elliptic leaf

Obovate leaf

Elliptic leaf   Obovate leaf

Obovate leaf

Elliptic leaf

H. × 'Franciscana'

3. *Veronica speciosa*
(Now *Hebe speciosa*)

H. × 'Franciscana Blue Gem'

A.1 *The characteristics of the three species responsible for* Hebe × 'Franciscana' *and*
H × 'Franciscana Blue Gem'

Appendix 2

THE ROYAL HORTICULTURAL SOCIETY 1982
HEBE TRIAL AT WISLEY GARDEN, SURREY

The following awards have been made to HEBES, by the Council of the Royal Horticultural Society, after trial at Wisley. (Issued March 1986.)

As Foliage Plants

First Class Certificate to:	*Hebe cupressoides* 'Boughton Dome'
Award of Merit to:	*Hebe buchananii*
	Hebe glaucophylla 'Variegata'
	Hebe 'Greensleeves' (raised by Mr G. Hutchins)
	Hebe 'Mrs Winder'
	Hebe ochracea
	Hebe ochracea 'James Stirling'
	Hebe pauciflora
	Hebe pinguifolia 'Pagei'
	Hebe rakaiensis
	Hebe topiaria
	Hebe vernicosa
	Hebe 'Waikiki'
Highly Commended to:	*Hebe carnosula*
	Hebe 'Douglasii'
	Hebe pauciramosa
	Hebe pimeleoides
	Hebe propinqua
	Hebe salicornioides
	Hebe 'Wingletye' (raised by Mr G. Hutchins)
Commended to:	*Hebe epacridea*

As Foliage and Flowering Plants

Award of Merit to:	*Hebe* 'Neil's Choice' (raised by Mr G. Hutchins)
	Hebe salicifolia
	Hebe 'Spender's Seedling'
Highly Commended to:	*Hebe* 'Warley' (*Hebe* 'Warleyensis')
Commended to:	*Hebe recurva*

As Flowering Plants

Award of Merit to:	*Hebe* 'Edington' (raised by Mr D. Chalk)
Highly Commended to:	*Hebe* 'Bowles' Hybrid'
	Hebe 'Purple Picture' (raised by Mr G. Hutchins)
Commended to:	*Hebe* 'Gauntlettii'

142

As Ground Cover Plants

Award of Merit to: *Hebe* 'Edinensis'
                            Hebe Albicans 'Sussex Carpet'
Commended to: *Hebe chathamica*

Appendix 3

SOME GARDENS TO VISIT IN BRITAIN
AND NEW ZEALAND

Britain

Collections of Hebe and Parahebe can be seen growing in these Gardens, which are usually open to the public. This list is in no way complete.

Abbey Gardens, Tresco, Isles of Scilly.
Cornwall County Council Demonstration Garden, Probus, near Truro, Cornwall.
Great Dixter Gardens (Mr Christopher Lloyd), Great Dixter, Northiam, East Sussex.
Harlow Car Gardens, Northern Horticultural Society, Harrogate, N. Yorkshire.
Inverewe Garden, National Trust for Scotland, Poolewe, Ross and Cromarty.
Logan Botanic Gardens, Port Logan, near Stranraer, Galloway, Scotland.
Marwood Hill Gardens (Dr Smart), near Barnstaple, N. Devon.
Rosemoor Garden Trust (Lady Ann Palmer), Great Torrington, N. Devon.
Royal Horticultural Society Garden, Wisley, near Woking, Surrey.
Savill Gardens, The Great Park, Windsor, Berkshire.
University of Bristol, Botanic Gardens, Leigh Woods, Bristol, Avon.
Ventnor Botanic Gardens, Ventnor, Isle of Wight.

New Zealand

North Island Auckland Regional Botanic Gardens, Manurewa, near Auckland.
Otari Native Plant Museum, Wellington.
Pukekura Park, New Plymouth.

South Island Cockayne Memorial Garden, Hagley Park, Christchurch.
Dunedin Botanic Garden, Dunedin.
Queen's Park (Native Plant Garden), Invercargill.

Appendix 4

THE HEBE SOCIETY

The Hebe Society was formed in February 1985 to encourage the growing of Hebes and allied New Zealand plants, and to assist in the conservation, improvement and research into the growing of Hebe, Parahebe and other allied plants.

A principal objective of the Society is to set up in South West England a National Reference Collection of Hebe Species and Cultivars. The registration of new cultivars will be undertaken by the Society in conjunction with the Registrar for the International Classification of Hebe in New Zealand.

The Society enables members to exchange information and advice in propagating and growing the many plant types and is developing a programme of lectures, visits to gardens and other places of horticultural interest, together with displays at plant shows and exhibitions.

Members are kept informed by quarterly News Letters listing events and information of interest to members of the Society. It is hoped to publish an Annual Bulletin with articles on Hebe culture and the growing of other New Zealand plants, including developments in New Zealand and elsewhere.

Application for membership should be made to the Hon. Treasurer, Hebe Society, 1 Woodpecker Drive, Hailsham, East Sussex BN27 3EZ.

The Secretary of the Hebe Society is Mr Geoffrey Scoble, who from mid September to April can be written to at: 'Rosemergy', Hain Walk, St Ives, Cornwall TR26 2AF and from May to mid September at 7 Friars Stile Road, Richmond-upon-Thames, Surrey TW10 6NH.

The address of the Registrar of the Hebe Society is 'Haygarth', Cleeton St Mary, Cleobury Mortimer, Kidderminster, Shropshire DY14 0QU

Bibliography

Dictionary of Gardening, Royal Horticultural Society (1951, Clarendon Press)

Flora of New Zealand, Volume 1, Dr H.H. Allan (1961, R.E. Owen, Govt. Printer)

Growing Native Plants, Barbara Matthews (1983, A.H. Reed)

New Zealand — Insight Guide (Harrap)

Ornamental Shrubs, C.E. Lucas Phillips & Peter Barber (1981, Cassell)

Our New Zealand Trees and Flowers, E.C. Richards (1947, Whitcombe and Tombs, now Whitcoull)

The Cultivation of New Zealand Trees and Shrubs, L.J. Metcalf (1972, A.H. Reed) (now fully revised, 1987, by L.J. Metcalf and published by Reed Methuen)

Trees and Shrubs Hardy in the British Isles, 4 vols., 8th edn, W.J. Bean (1973, Murray).

Glossary

anther	the pollen bearing part of a stamen.
adpressed	pressed against, such as whipcord leaves to the stem.
appressed	lying flat against a surface, like hairs on a leaf.
axil	the upper angle between the leaf stalk and stem.
bifarious	arranged in two opposite rows.
capsule	a dry fruit that splits.
ciliate	fringed with hairs along the margin.
concave	depressed, like a saucer.
convex	raised, opposite of concave — upside down saucer.
corolla	the petals of a flower whether free or joined together.
corymb	a flat topped or slightly convex flower or inflorescence.
deciduous	losing its leaves in autumn.
decumbent	lying flat or horizontal, but ascending at the outward ends.
deflexed	turned abruptly downwards.
deltoid	broadly triangular.
distichous	arranged in two opposite rows, so as to lie in one plane.
domatia	short oblique pits on the under surface of the leaves in *H.townsonii*.
downy	covered in fine silk like hairs.
elliptic	shaped like an ellipse and rounded at both ends with the middle the widest point.
fasciation	lateral stem shoots that have not separated normally but grow together forming a flattened stem, which is often wider than the normal stem. In *H.*'Girwoodiana' the buds towards the apex of the spike grow together forming this flattened end.
fastigiate	branches close together and erect.
glabrous	smooth and having no hairs, pubescence or down.
glaucous	a distinctly bluish green colour, not due to bloom.
growing point	the growing or extending bud at the end of a shoot or stem.
inflorescence	an overall or general term for a flower or collection of flowers on a plant.
internode	that part of a stem between the axils or nodes on a stem.
keeled	a sharp, distinct ridge, like the keel of a boat.
lamina	thin, flat, as in the blade of a leaf.
lanceolate	shaped like a lance head, pointed at the top, ovate at the bottom.
lateral	refers to a side shoot or branch.

linear	narrow, elongated and with parallel margins.
midrib	the main central vein of a leaf.
node	that part of the stem from which the leaf or leaves arise.
ob-	before a word signifies inversion.
oblanceolate	inversion of lanceolate — rounded at the top and pointed at the bottom, or at the stem end in the case of a leaf.
oblong	much longer than broader
obovate	like an egg with the broadest part towards the top or apex.
orbicular	rounded in outline as applied to a leaf. Circular.
ovate	like an egg with the narrowest part towards the apex.
panicle	an irregular, loose arrangement of flowers on a stem; also includes a branched raceme and a corymb.
pedicel	the stalk supporting a single flower in a compound arrangement of flowers.
petiole	the stalk of a leaf.
pubescent	covered in short, soft hairs.
raceme	an unbranched, elongated arrangement of stalked flowers.
rupestral	growing on rocks.
serrate	sharply toothed with teeth pointing forward towards the apex.
sessile	leaf or flower without a stalk.
sinus	the recess or gap at the base of a pair of unopened leaves.
spathulate	spoon shaped.
spike	an unbranched, elongated arrangement of flowers, with the lower flowers opening first.
tetra-	prefix meaning four.
variety	a subdivision of a species differing in certain defined characters from the species.

Index

Hebe Species, Varieties and Cultivars